THE WHITE BOOK

50 Showstoppers

782.81

Wise Publications
London/New York/Paris/Sydney/Copenhagen/Madrid

Exclusive Distributors:
Music Sales Limited
8-9 Frith Street,
London W1V 5TZ, England.
Music Sales Pty Limited
120 Rothschild Avenue,
Rosebery, NSW 2018,
Australia.

Order No. AM953843
ISBN 0-7119-7189-7
This book © Copyright 1998 by Wise Publications

Compiled by Peter Evans
Cover design by Studio Twenty, London.

Printed in the United Kingdom by
The Bath Press, Bath

Your Guarantee of Quality
As publishers, we strive to produce every book to the
highest commercial standards.
This book has been carefully designed to minimise awkward
page turns and to make playing from it a real pleasure.
Particular care has been given to specifying acid-free,
neutral-sized paper made from pulps which have not been
elemental chlorine bleached. This pulp is from farmed
sustainable forests and was produced with special regard
for the environment. Throughout, the printing and binding
have been planned to ensure a sturdy, attractive publication
which should give years of enjoyment.
If your copy fails to meet our high standards,
please inform us and we will gladly replace it.

Music Sales' complete catalogue describes thousands of titles
and is available in full colour sections by subject, direct from
Music Sales Limited. Please state your areas of interest and
send a cheque/postal order for £1.50 for postage to:
Music Sales Limited, Newmarket Road, Bury St. Edmunds,
Suffolk IP33 3YB.

A Woman In Love

Words & Music by Frank Loesser

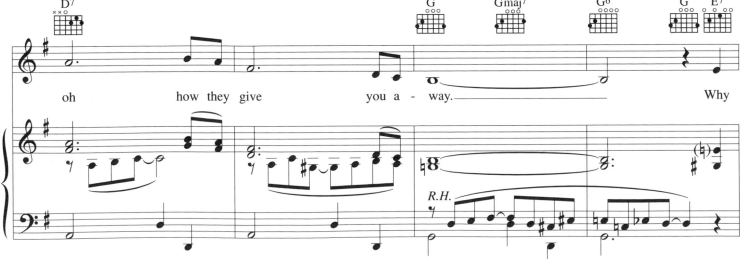

5

Ain't Misbehavin'

Words by Andy Razaf
Music by Thomas Waller & Harry Brooks

are worth wait - in' for, be - - lieve me.

I don't stay out late, don't care to go,

I'm home a - bout eight, just

me and my ra - di - o, Ain't Mis - be - hav - in',

I'm sav - in' my love for

you.

9

And This Is My Beloved

Words & Music by Robert Wright & George Forrest

Andante cantabile

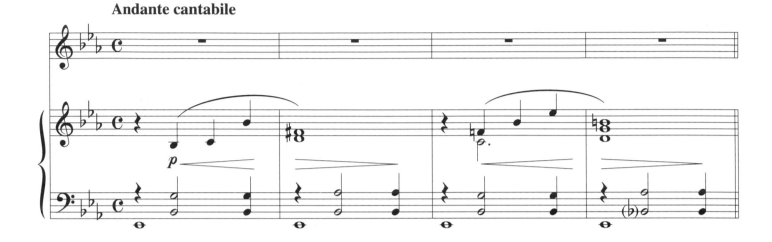

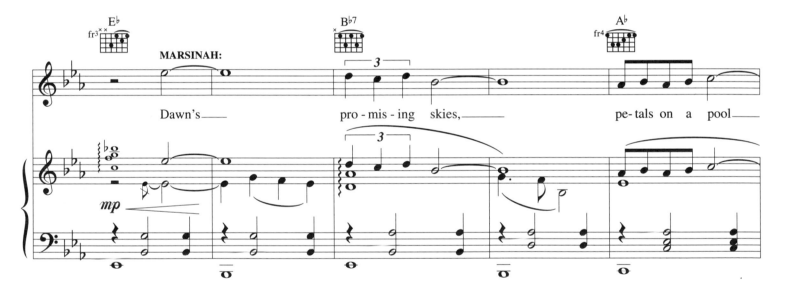

MARSINAH:

Dawn's ___ pro-mis-ing skies, ___ pe-tals on a pool ___

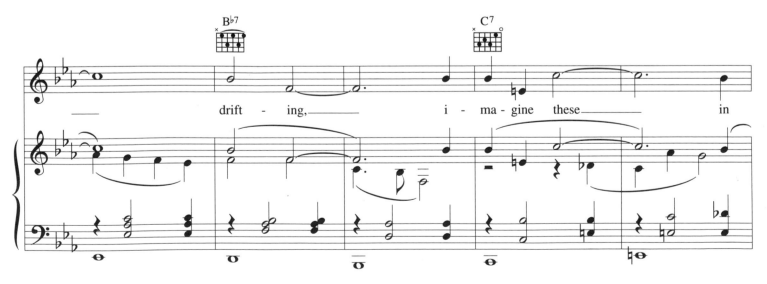

___ drift-ing, ___ i-ma-gine these ___ in

11

lov - ed.___ And when {she he} speaks, and when {she he}

talks to me, mu - sic!___ Mys - te - ry!___ And when {she he}

moves, and when {she he} walks with me, pa - ra - dise___ comes sud - den - ly

near!___ All that can stir,___ all that can stun,___

accel. e cresc. poco a poco

mf

mp

sempre accel.

mf

f

largamente

ff

13

Any Dream Will Do

Music by Andrew Lloyd Webber
Lyrics by Tim Rice

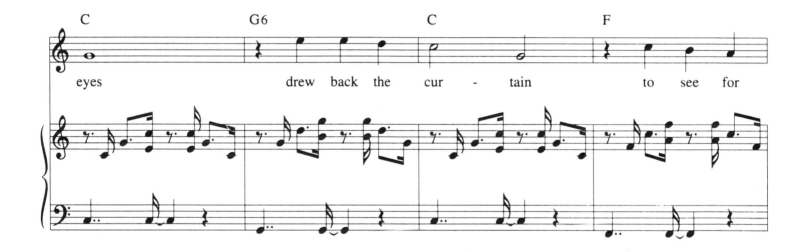

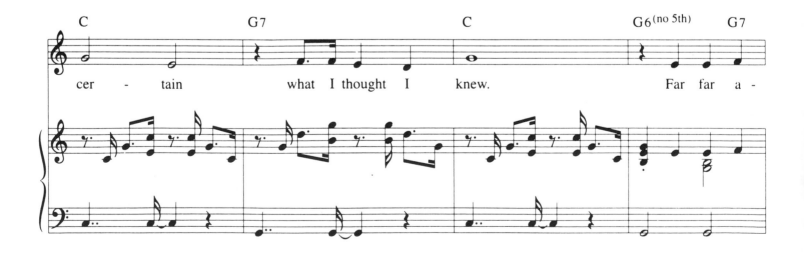

way some-one was weep - ing, but the world was

sleep - ing, a - ny dream will do. I wore my

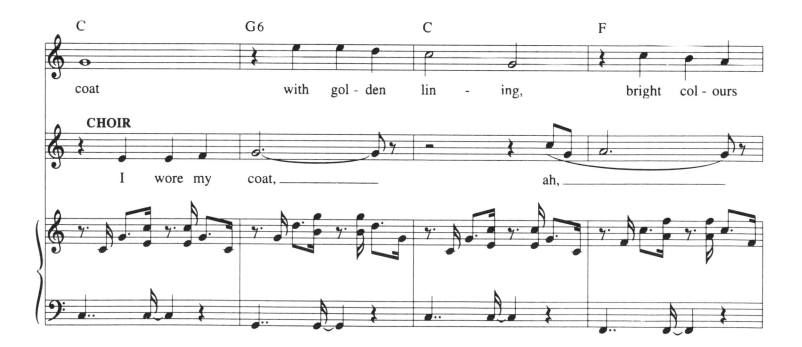

coat with gol - den lin - ing, bright col-ours

CHOIR

I wore my coat, _____ ah, _____

15

16

crash of drums __ a flash of light, __ my gold-en coat flew out of sight. __ The

CHOIR

The

col-ours fad-ed in-to dark-ness, I was left a-lone. __

col-ours fad-ed in-to dark-ness, ah, __ ah, __

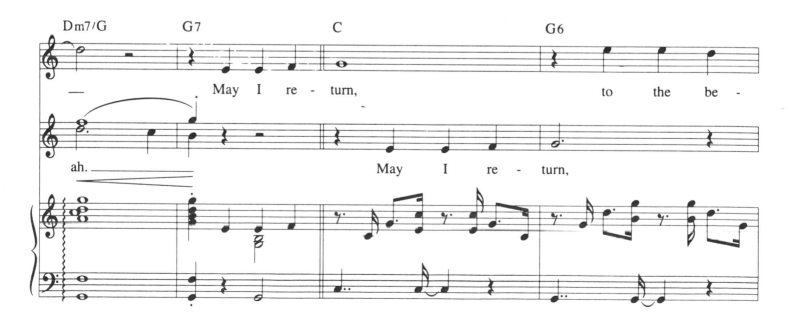

May I re-turn, to the be-

ah. __ May I re-turn,

Another Suitcase In Another Hall

Music by Andrew Lloyd Webber
Lyrics by Tim Rice

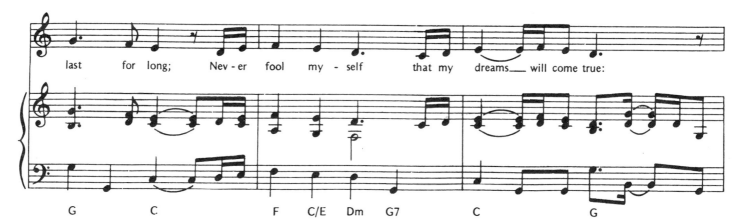

go - ing to? _____

ten.

Don't ask an - y -

rall.   ten.

rall.

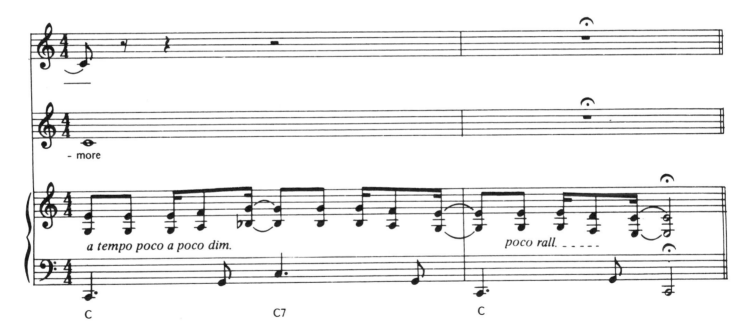

- more

a tempo poco a poco dim.

poco rall. _ _ _ _ _

C

C7

C

Additional Lyrics

2. Time and time again I've said that I don't care;
   That I'm immune to gloom, that I'm hard through and through:
   But every time it matters all my words desert me;
   So anyone can hurt me - and they do.

   So what happens now? . . . . etc., as above.

3. Call in three months' time and I'll be fine I know;
   Well maybe not that fine, but I'll survive anyhow:
   I won't recall the names and places of this sad occasion;
   But that's no consolation, here and now.

   So what happens now? . . . . etc., as above.

As Long As He Needs Me

Words & Music by Lionel Bart

used so ill?____ He knows I al - ways will,____ as long as

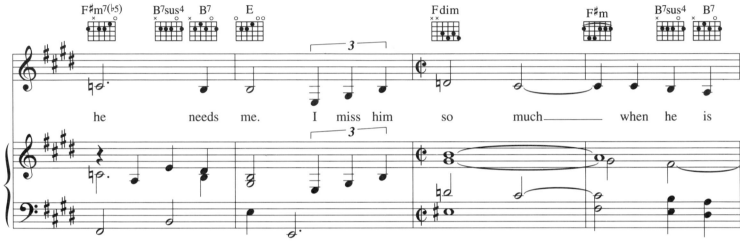

he needs me. I miss him so much____ when he is

gone. But when he's near me,____ I don't let

on.____ The way I feel in - side,____ the love I

24

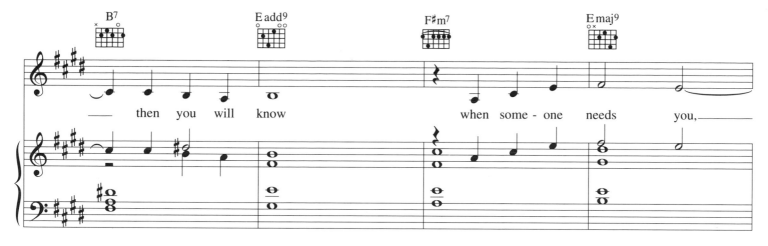

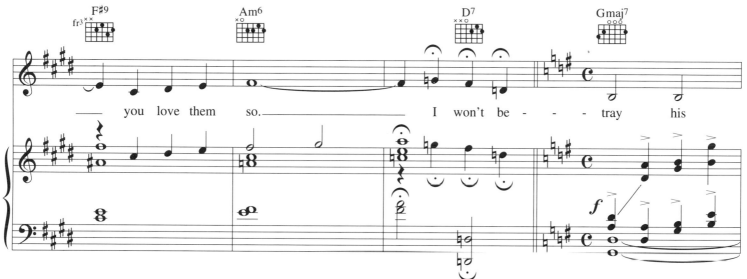

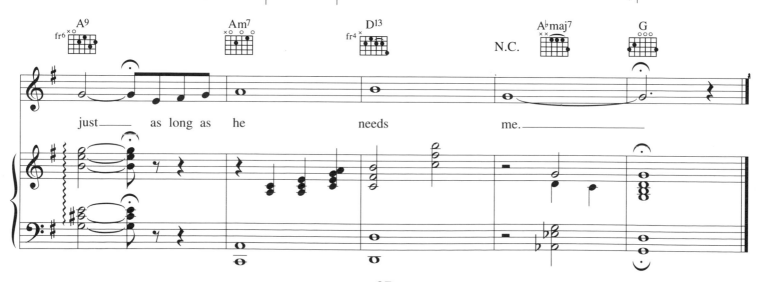

27

Big D

Words & Music by Frank Loesser

Brightly

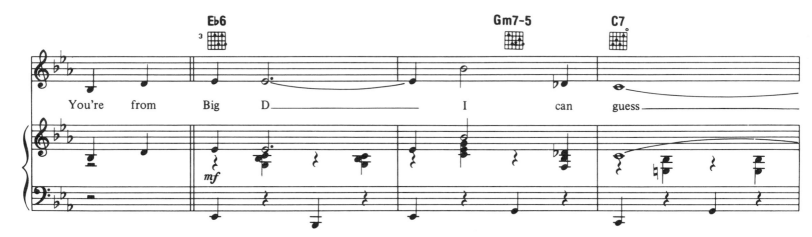

You're from Big D _____ I can guess

by the way you drawl_____ and the way you dress

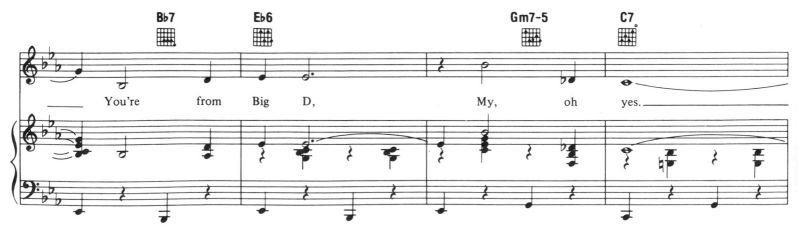

You're from Big D, My, oh yes. _____

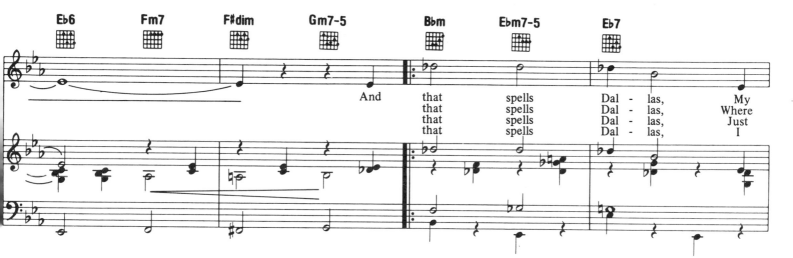

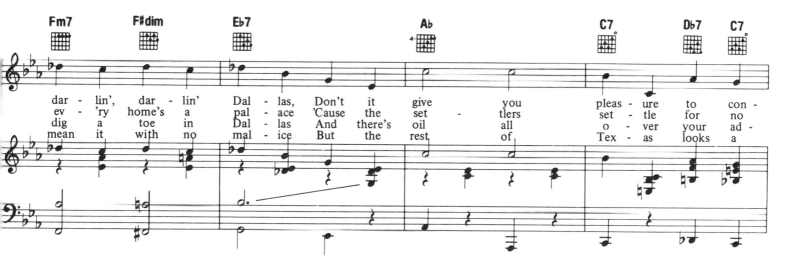

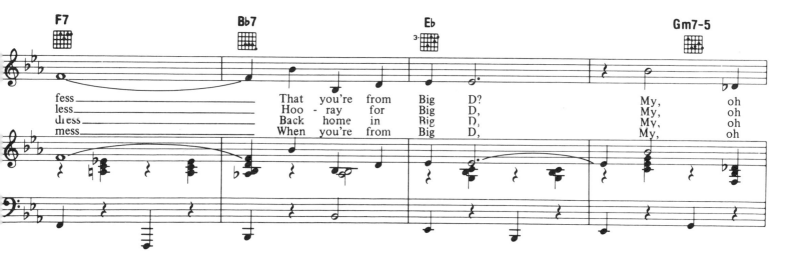

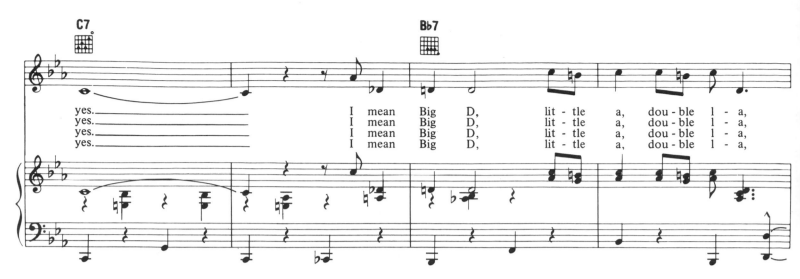

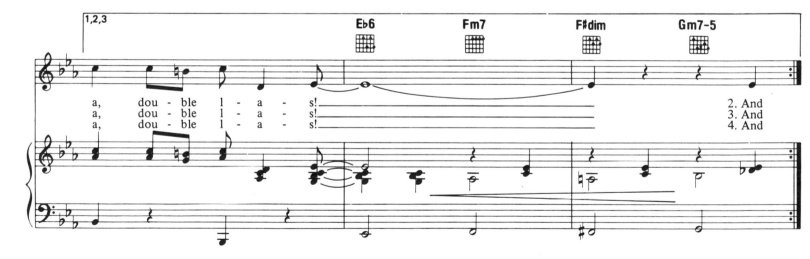

Broadway Baby

Words & Music by Stephen Sondheim

To Coda ⊕

Coda

Cabaret

Music by John Kander
Lyrics by Fred Ebb

Moderato

What good is sit-ting a-lone in your room?
Put down the knit-ting, the book and the broom,

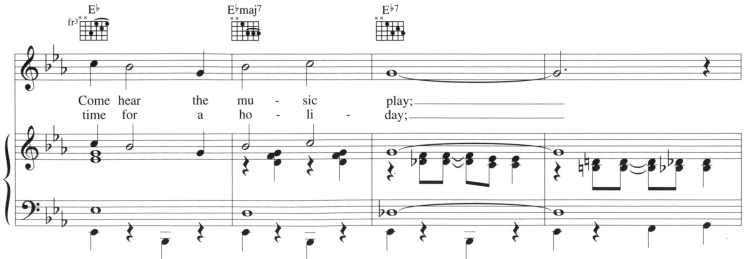

Come hear the mu-sic play;
time for a ho-li-day;

1. No use per - mit - ting some proph - et of doom, _____ to
2. Start by ad - mit - ting some from cra - dle to tomb _____

wipe ev - 'ry smile a - way; _____
is n't that long a stay; _____

To Coda ⊕
(Last time)

Life is a cab - a - ret, old chum _____

come to the cab - a - ret. _____ Come taste the

N.C.

38

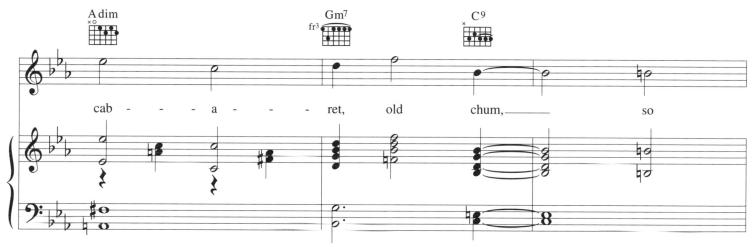

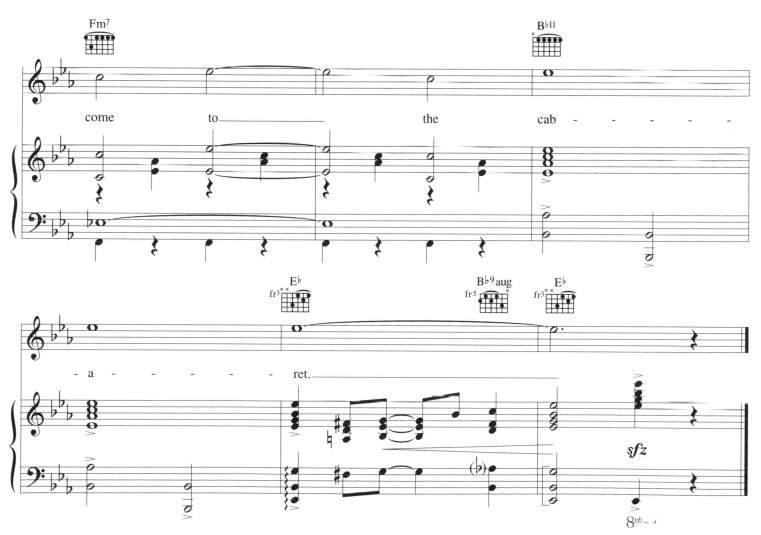

Castle On A Cloud

Music by Claude-Michel Schönberg. Lyrics by Herbert Kretzmer.
Original Text by Alain Boublil & Jean-Marc Natel

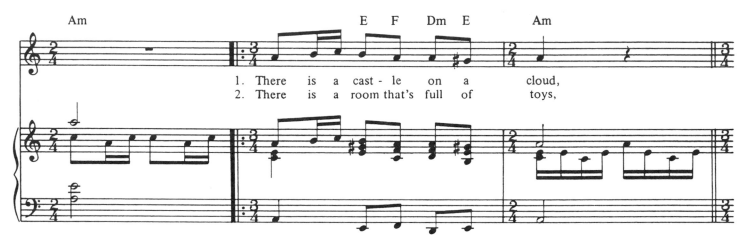

40

3. There is a la-dy all in white ___ holds me and sings a lul-la-by. She's
nice to see and she's soft to touch; she says 'Cos-ette, I love you very much.' I know a place where no-one's
lost, I know a place where no-one cries.
Cry-ing at all is not al-lowed, Not in my cast-le on a cloud.

Company

Music & Lyrics by Stephen Sondheim

Phone rings, door chimes, in comes com-pa-ny!

No strings, good times, just chums, com-pa-ny!

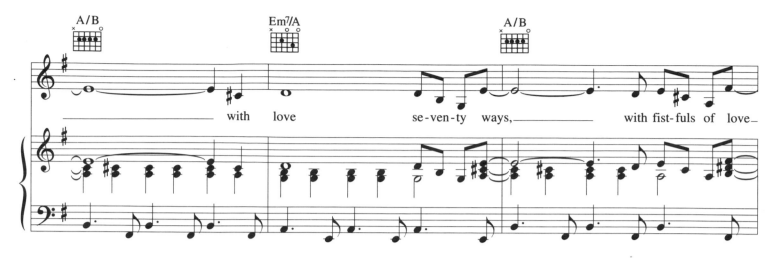

with love   se-ven-ty ways,_____   with fist-fuls of love__

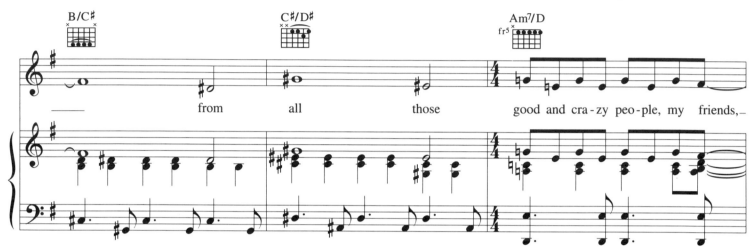

from   all   those   good and cra-zy peo-ple, my   friends,__

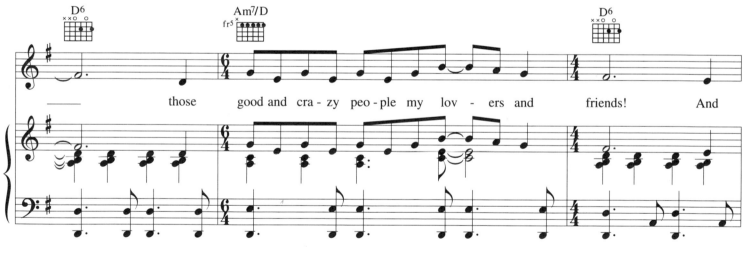

those   good and cra-zy peo-ple my   lov-ers and   friends!   And

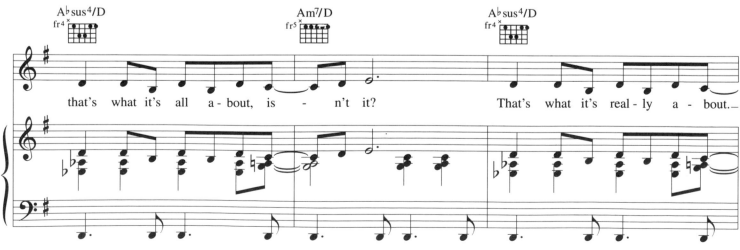

that's what it's all a-bout, is - n't it?   That's what it's real-ly a-bout.__

Climb Ev'ry Mountain

Words by Oscar Hammerstein II
Music by Richard Rodgers

Consider Yourself

Words & Music by Lionel Bart

Moderate march tempo

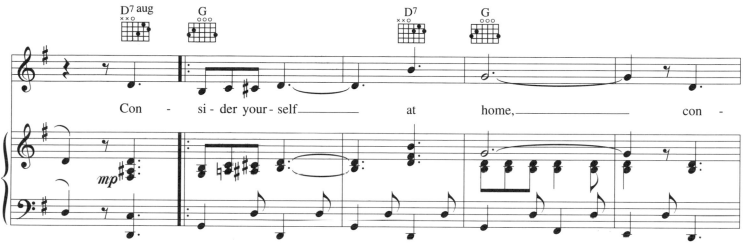

Con - si - der your-self ___ at home, ___ con -

si - der your-self ___ one of the fa - mi - ly. ___ I've
We've

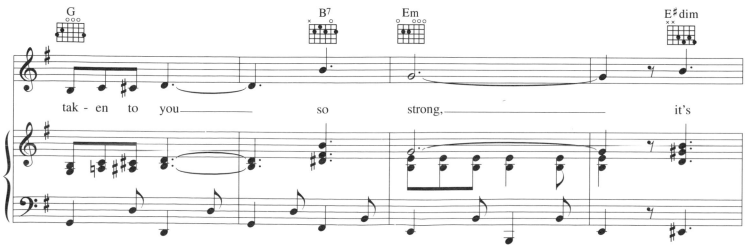

tak - en to you ___ so strong, ___ it's

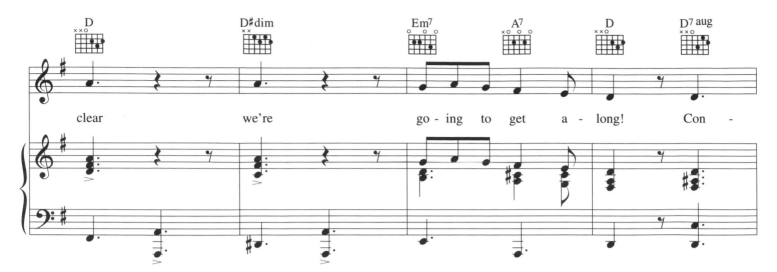

clear we're go-ing to get a-long! Con -

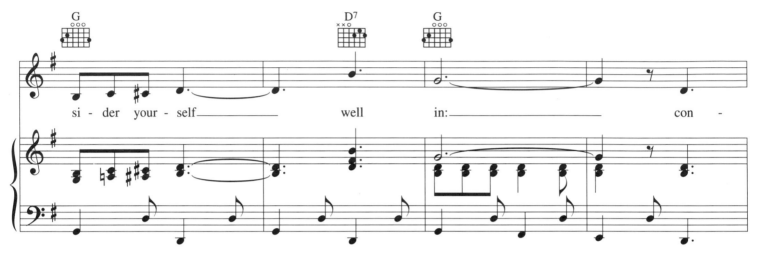

si - der your - self____ well in:____ con -

si - der your - self____ part of the fur - ni - ture.____ There

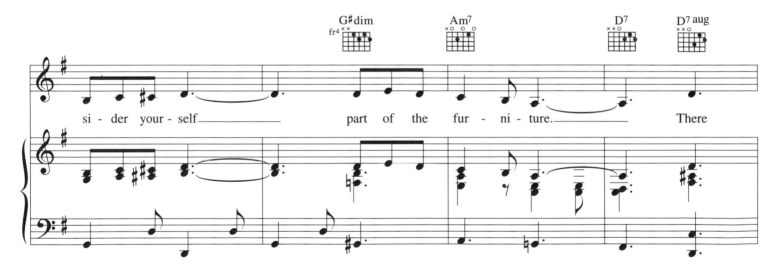

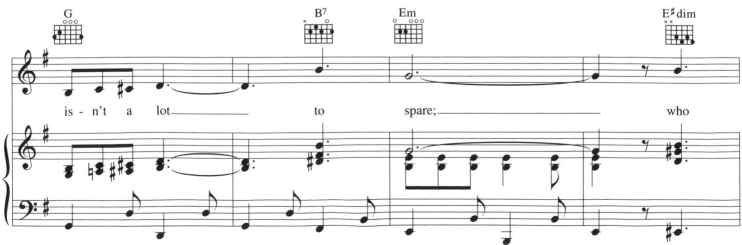

is - n't a lot____ to spare;____ who

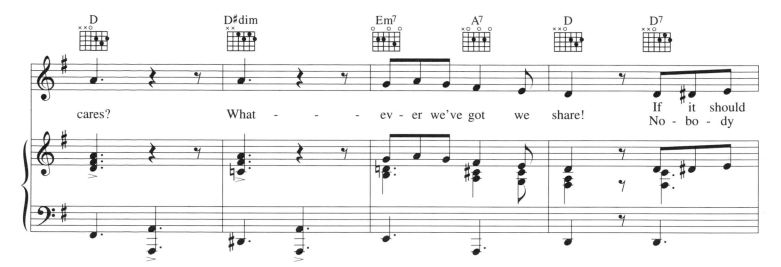

cares? What - - ev - er we've got we share! If it should
No - bo - dy

chance to be we should see some hard - er days,____
tries to be lah - di - dah and up - pi - ty,

emp - ty lard - er days,_____ why grouse?_____
there's a cup o' tea_____ for all.

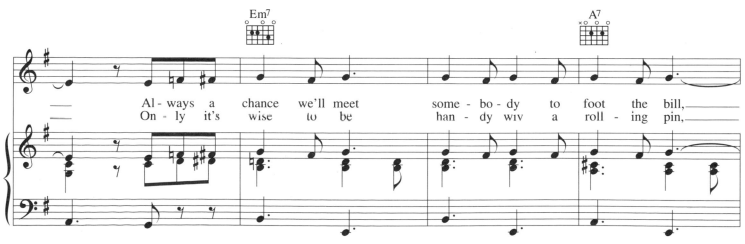

Al - ways a chance we'll meet some - bo - dy to foot the bill,____
On - ly it's wise to be han - dy wiv a roll - ing pin,

51

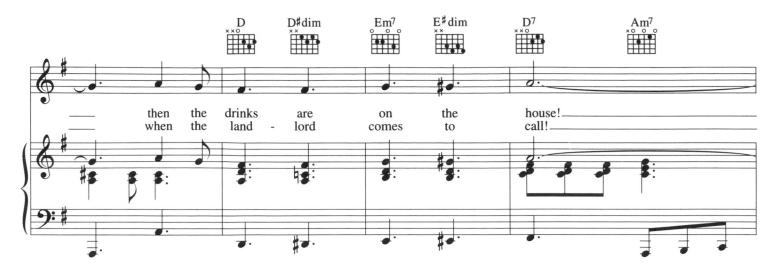

then the drinks are on the house!
when the land - lord comes to call!

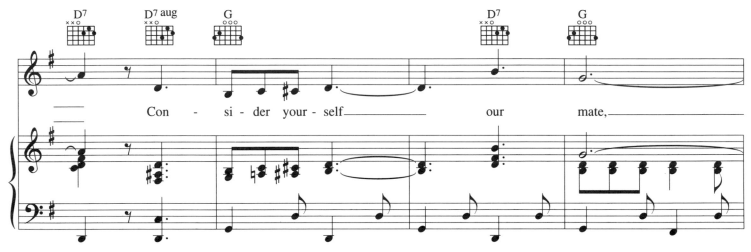

Con - si - der your - self _____ our mate, _____

we don't want to have _____ no fuss. _____

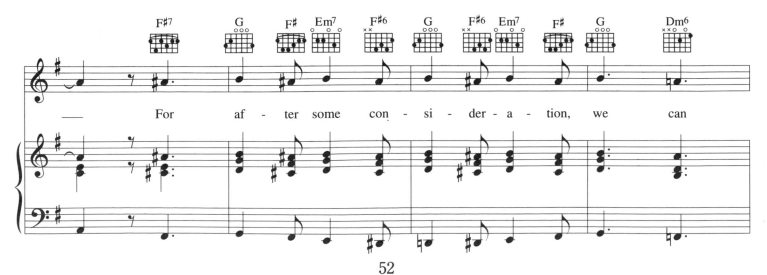

For af - ter some con - si - der - a - tion, we can

state: con - - si - der your-self_____ one of

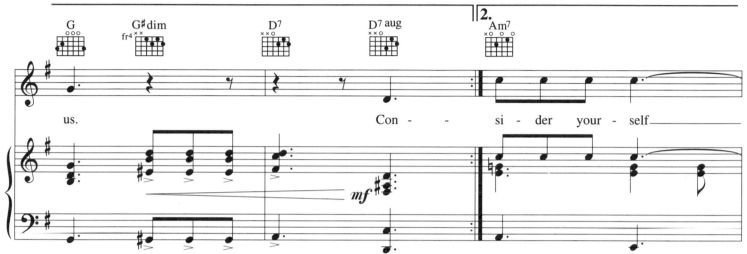

1.

us. Con - - si - der your-self_____

mf

2.

one of

cresc.

us._____

ff

53

Diamonds Are A Girl's Best Friend

Words by Leo Robin
Music by Jule Styne

60

Do You Hear The People Sing?

Music by Claude-Michel Schönberg. Lyric by Herbert Kretzmer.
Original Text by Alain Boublil & Jean-Marc Natel

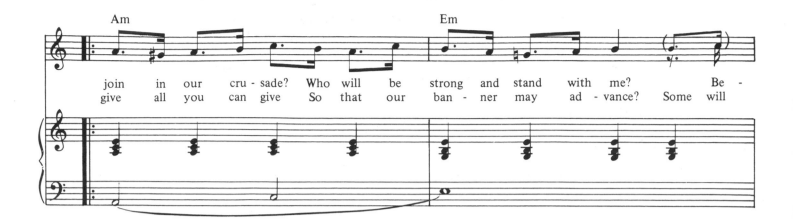

join in our cru - sade? Who will be strong and stand with me? Be -
give all you can give So that our ban - ner may ad - vance? Some will

- yond the bar - ri - cade Is there a world you ___ long to see? Then
fall, and some will live. Will you stand up and ___ take your chance? The

join in the fight That will give you the right to be free!
blood of the mar - tyrs Will wa - ter the mea - dows of France!

Do you

cresc.

hear the peo - ple sing? Sing - ing the song of an - gry men? It is the

mu - sic of a peo - ple Who will not be slaves a - gain! When the

beat - ing of your heart Echoes the beat - ing of the drums, There is a life a - bout to start When to - mor - row

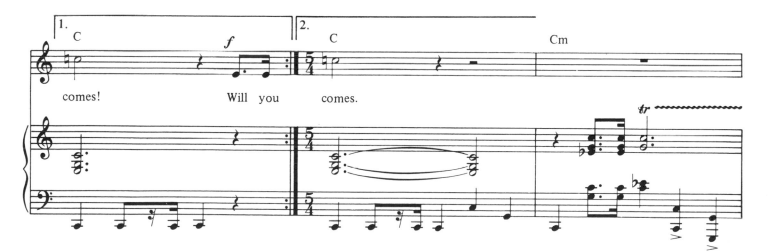

comes! Will you comes.

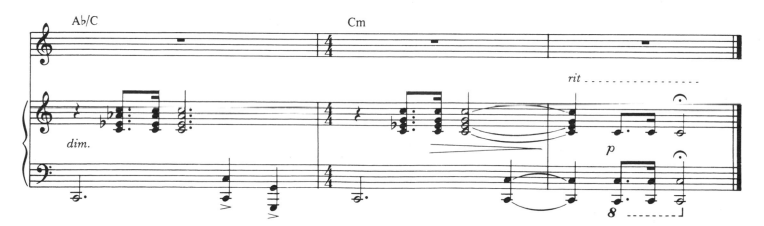

63

Don't Cry For Me Argentina

Music by Andrew Lloyd Webber
Lyrics by Tim Rice

So I chose free - dom Run-ning a - round try-ing

ev - 'ry - thing new, but noth - ing im-pressed me at all, I

nev - er ex - pect - ed it to. Don't cry for me Ar-gen -

ti - na _____ the truth is I nev - er left you. All through my

rall.

mp - f a tempo

all you have to do is look at me to know that ev-'ry word is true.

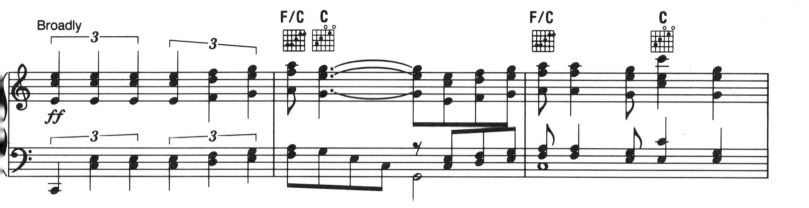

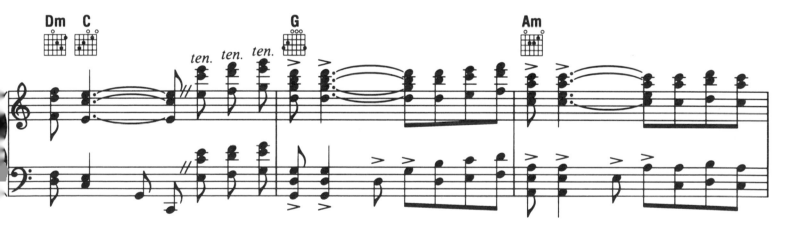

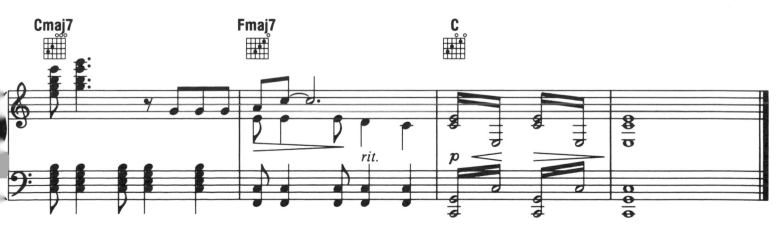

Edelweiss

Words by Oscar Hammerstein II
Music by Richard Rodgers

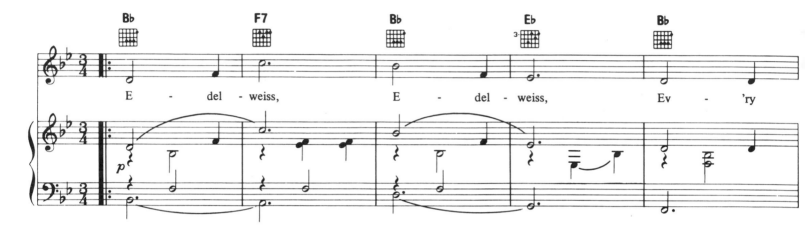

E - del - weiss, E - del - weiss, Ev - 'ry

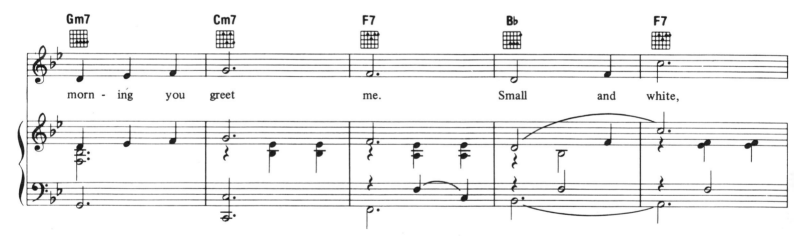

morn - ing you greet me. Small and white,

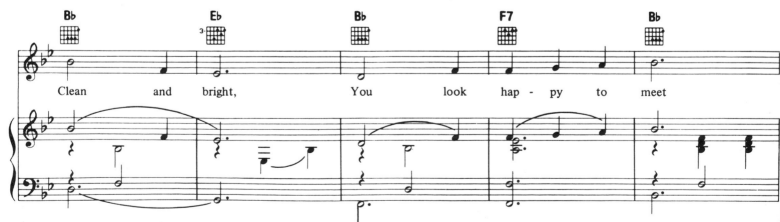

Clean and bright, You look hap - py to meet

71

Everything's Alright

Music by Andrew Lloyd Webber
Lyrics by Tim Rice

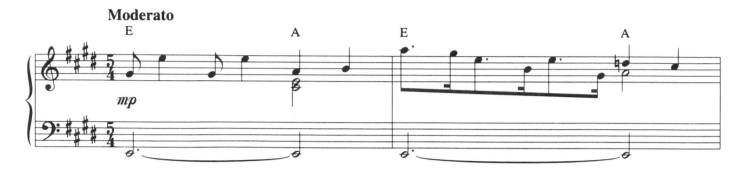

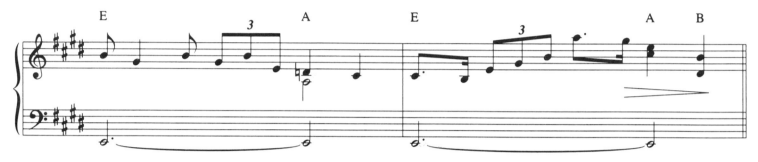

(1, %) Try not to get wor - ried, try not to turn on to pro - blems that up - set you.
(2.) Sleep and I shall soothe you, calm you and a - noint you, Myrrh for your hot fore - head.

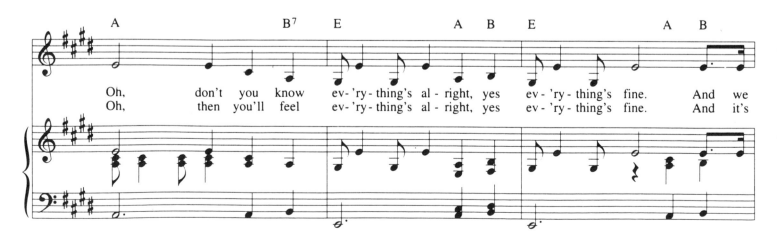

Oh, don't you know ev - 'ry - thing's al - right, yes ev - 'ry - thing's fine. And we
Oh, then you'll feel ev - 'ry - thing's al - right, yes ev - 'ry - thing's fine. And it's

To Coda ⊕
no repeat on D.%.

ROCK

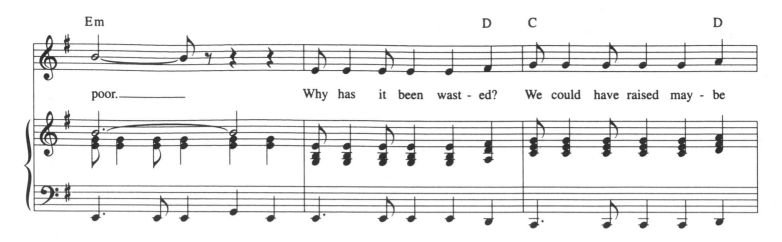

poor.＿＿＿ Why has it been wast-ed? We could have raised may - be

three hun-dred sil-ver pie-ces or more.＿＿＿ Peo-ple who are hun-gry,

peo-ple who are starv-ing mat - ter more＿ than

your feet and hair.＿＿＿＿＿＿＿＿＿＿＿

⊕ *Coda*

JESUS

Sure - ly you're not say - ing we have the re - sour - ces to save the poor from their

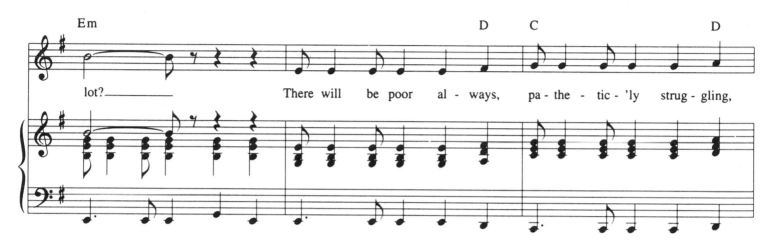

lot?_____ There will be poor al - ways, pa - the - tic - 'ly strug - gling,

look at the good things you've got!_____ Think! While you still have me.

Move! While you still see me. You'll be lost,_____ you'll be so_____ so_____

75

Light Rock

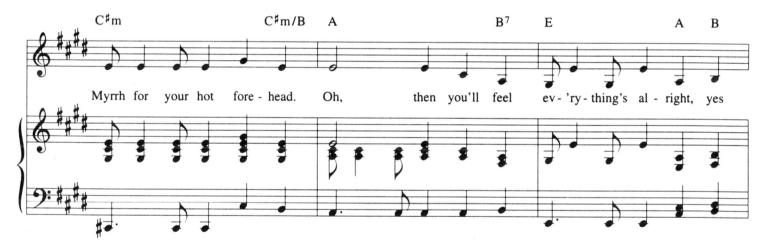

for the fire—— in your head and feet.—— Close your

APOSTLES' WOMEN

eyes, close your eyes and re-lax, think of no-thing to - night.—— Close your eyes, close your eyes and re-

Hard Rock

Repeat many times, crescendo to f then fade

lax, think of no-thing to - night. Close your
Ev-'ry-thing's al - right, yes ev-'ry-thing's al-right, yes

Floor Show

Words & Music by Richard O'Brien

It was great when it all be - gan,_____ I was a
(Verse 2 see block lyric)

re - gu - lar Fran - kie fan,_____ but it was ov - er when he had the plan

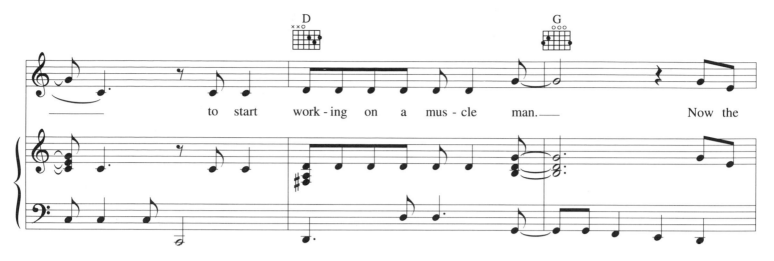

to start work-ing on a mus-cle man.___ Now the

on - ly thing that gives me hope___ is my love of a cer-tain dope___

rose tints my world, keeps me safe from my trou - ble and pain.___

2. I'm It's be - -

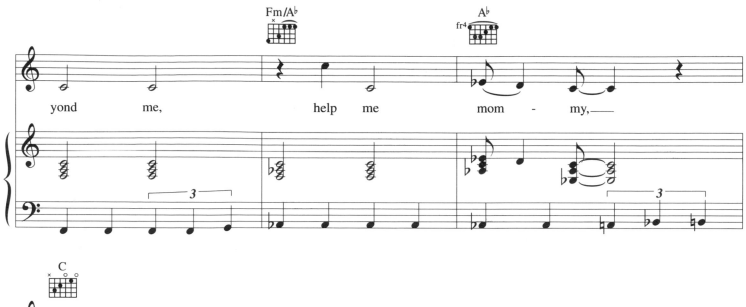

yond me, help me mom - my, ____

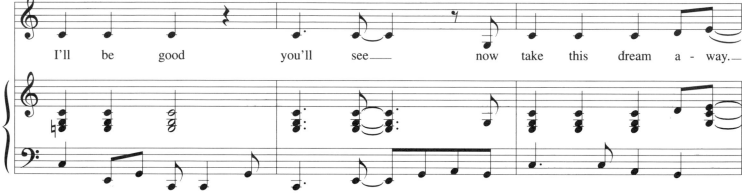

I'll be good you'll see ____ now take this dream a - way. ____

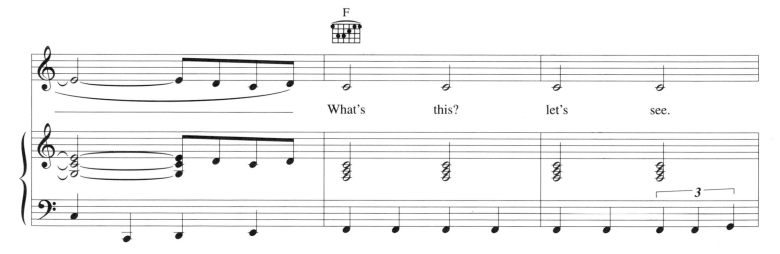

What's this? let's see.

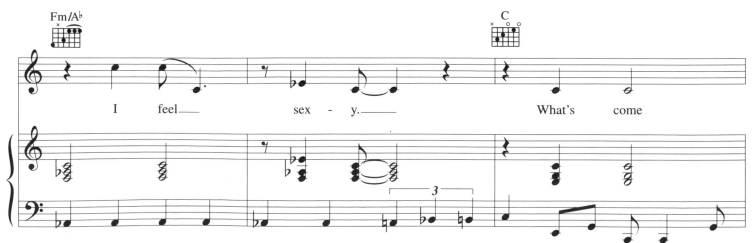

I feel ____ sex - y. ____ What's come

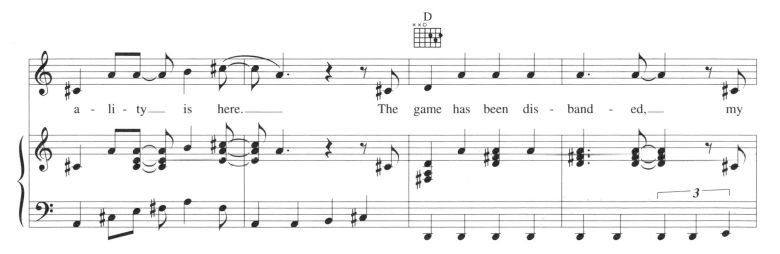

81

mind has been___ ex - pand - ed,___ it's a gas that Frank - y's land - ed,___ his

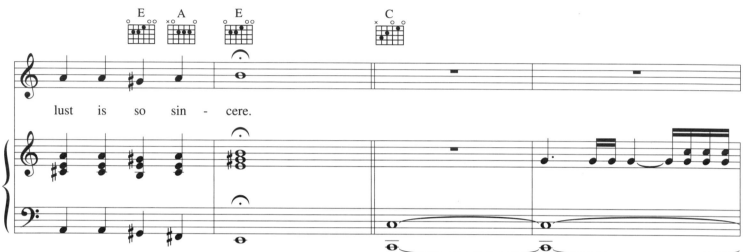

lust is so sin - cere.

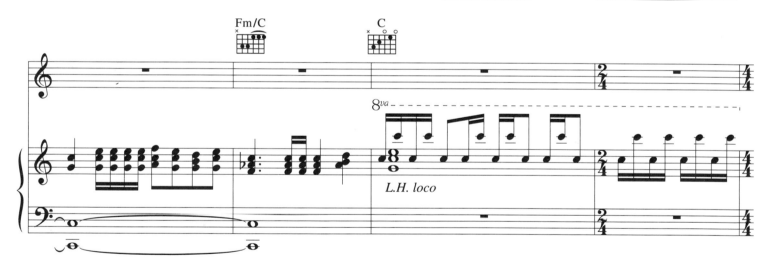

84

hit and your mind goes ping! Your heart-'ll thump and your blood will sing so let the

par - ty and the sounds rock on.___ I'm gon - na shake it till the life has gone,___

rose tint my world, keep me safe from my trou - ble and pain.___

I'm a ___   I'm a

3. Slower

Frank - n - fur - ter, it's all ov - er, your mis - sion is a fail - ure, your life-style's too ex - treme.— I'm your new com-mand - er, you are now my pri - son - er, we re - turn to Tran-syl - va - nia, pre - pare the tran - sit beam.

Verse 2:
I'm just seven hours old
And truly beautiful to behold
And somebody should be told
My libido hasn't been controlled.
Now the only thing I've come to trust
Is an orgasmic rush of lust
Rose tints my world
Keeps me safe from my trouble and pain.

Gonna Build A Mountain

Words & Music by Leslie Bricusse & Anthony Newley

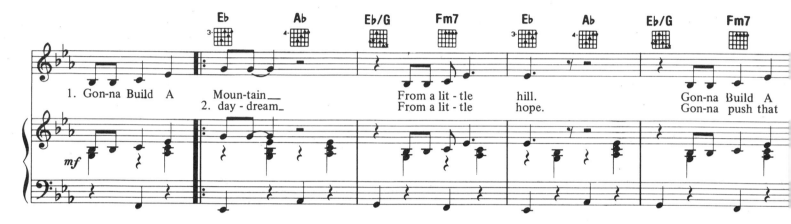

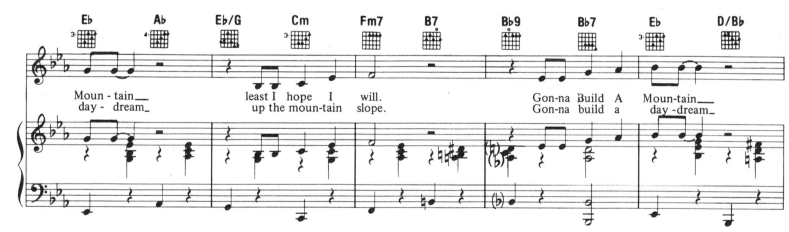

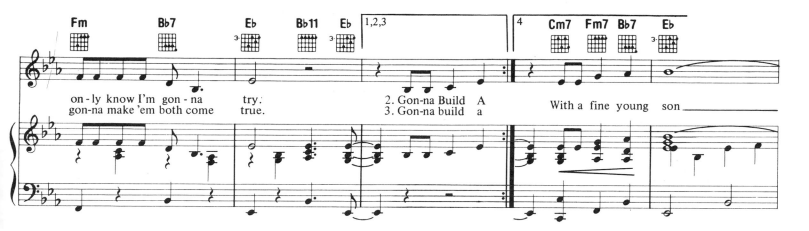

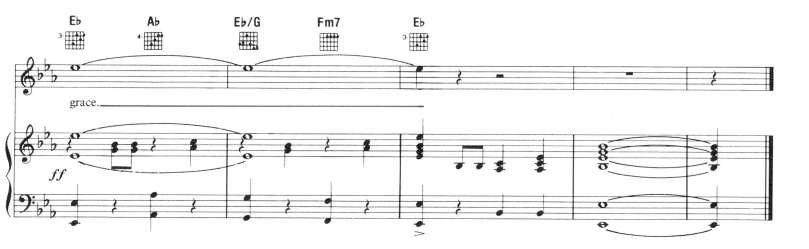

Verse 3. Gon-na build a heaven from a little hell.
Gon-na build a heaven and I know darn well.
If I build my mountain with a lot of care.
And take my daydream up the mountain heaven
will be waiting there.

Verse 4. When I've built that heaven as I will some day
And the Lord sends Gabriel to take me away,
Wanna fine young son to take my place
I'll leave a son in my heav-en on earth,
With the Lord's good grace.

Good Morning Starshine

Words by James Rado & Gerome Ragni
Music by Galt MacDermot

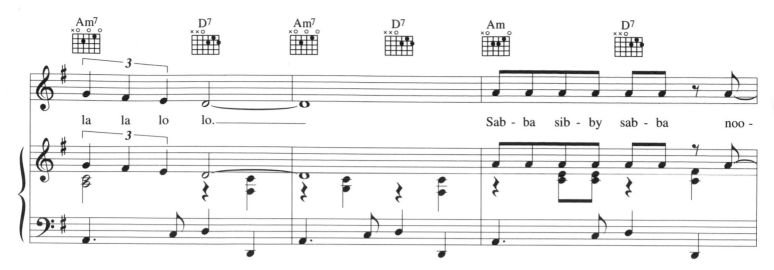

la la lo lo._____ Sab - ba sib - by sab - ba noo-

-by ab - ba nab - ba le le lo lo._____

Too - by oo - by wal - la noo - by ab - ba nab - ba, ear - ly morn - ing sing - ing song.—

1.
N.C.
_____ Good morn - ing _____
mp

2.
Sing - ing a song,
mf

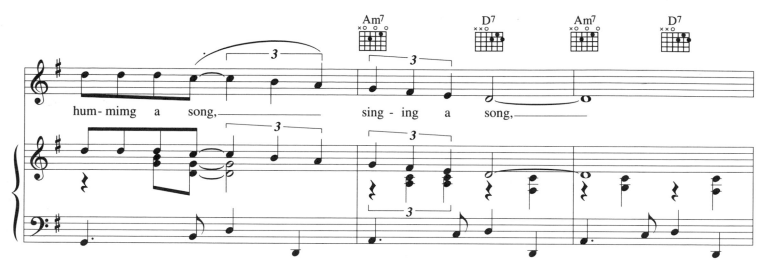

hum-mimg a song,_____ sing-ing a song,_____

lov-ing a song,____ laugh-ing a song,____ sing____ the song,____

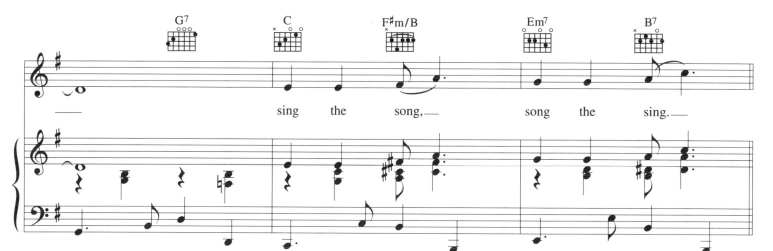

sing the song,____ song the sing.____

Repeat to fade

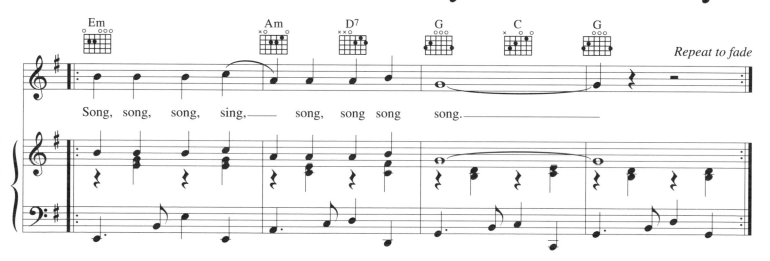

Song, song, song, sing,____ song, song song song.____

93

I Ain't Down Yet

Words & Music by Meredith Willson

March tempo

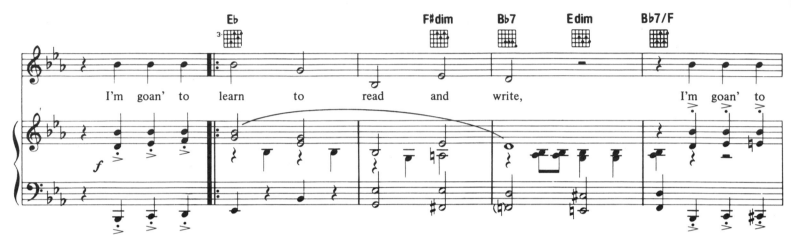

I'm goan' to learn to read and write, I'm goan' to

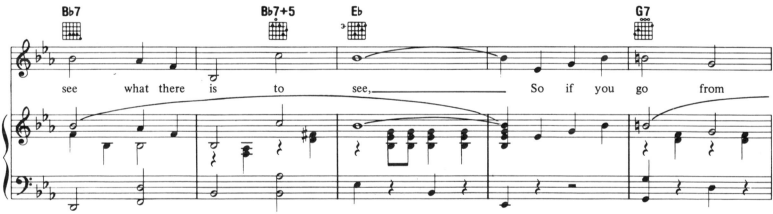

see what there is to see, So if you go from

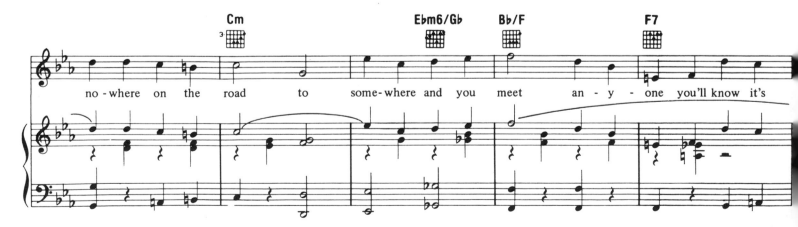

no - where on the road to some - where and you meet an - y - one you'll know it's

95

I Can Do That

Words by Edward Kleban
Music by Marvin Hamlisch

I Believe In You

Words & Music by Frank Loesser

You have the cool clear eyes of a seek-er of wis-dom and truth,
sound of good sol-id judg-ment when-ev-er you talk,

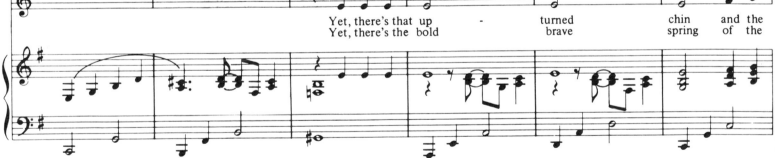

Yet, there's that up - turned chin and the
Yet, there's the bold brave spring of the

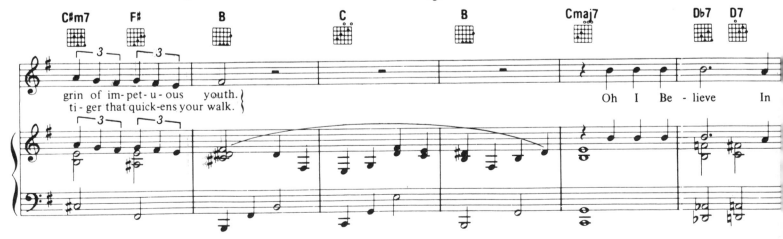

grin of im-pet-u-ous youth.
ti - ger that quick-ens your walk.

Oh I Be - lieve In

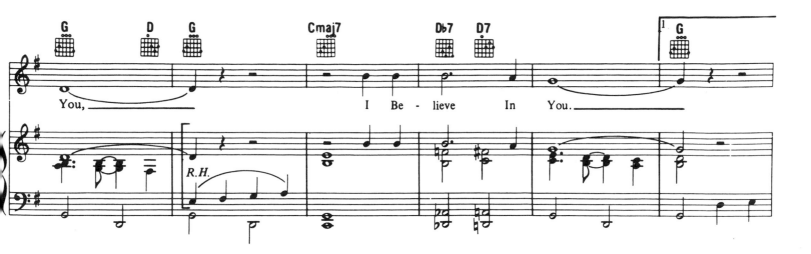

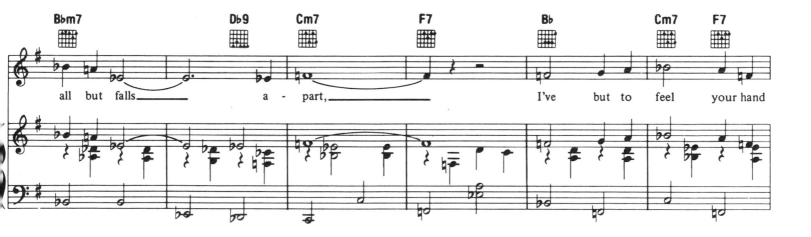

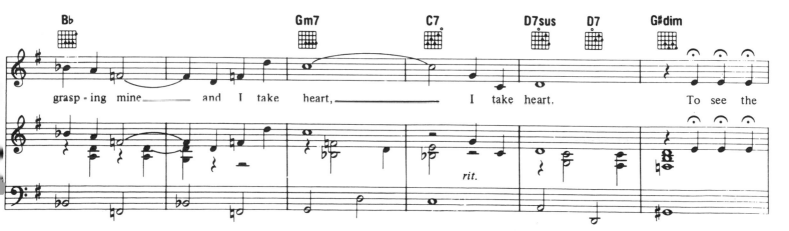

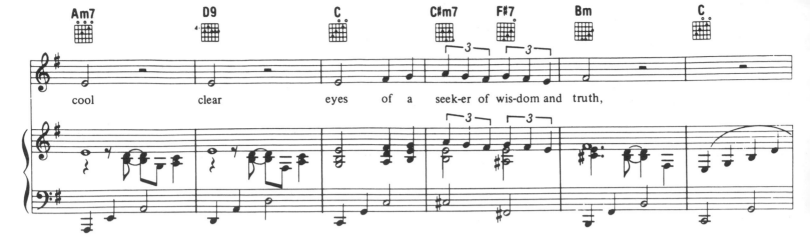

cool   clear   eyes of a seek-er of wis-dom and truth,

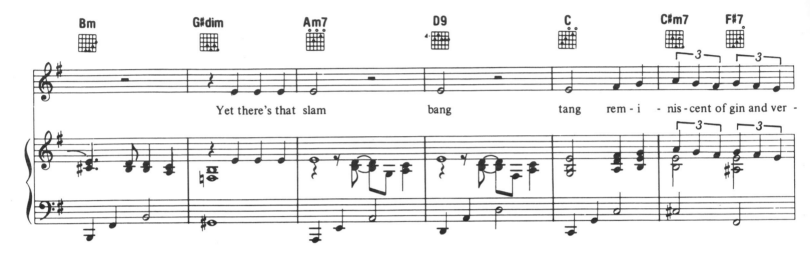

Yet there's that slam   bang   tang rem - i - nis - cent of gin and ver -

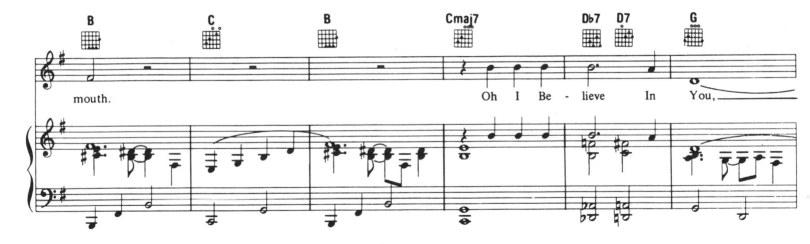

mouth.   Oh I Be - lieve In You, ____

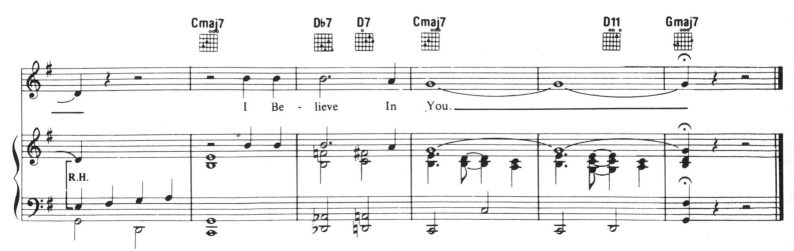

I Be - lieve In You. ____

I Dreamed A Dream
(From the Musical 'Les Misérables')

Music by Claude-Michel Schönberg. Lyric by Herbert Kretzmer.
Original Text by Alain Boublil & Jean-Marc Natel

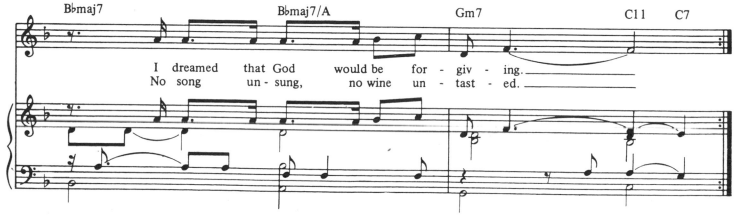

I Will Make You Proud

Music by Claude-Michel Schönberg
Lyrics by Alain Boublil, Edward Hardy & Herbert Kretzmer

cursed but ne - ver cowed, in the call of du - ty, I will make you proud. Gas-

ton, I knew your fa - ther. Ma - ras, I knew yours too. Men who stoop for de - cen - cy

just the same as you. Sons, do not be - tray them, daugh - ters, do not fail.

In the face of pe - ril good - ness shall pre - vail. Stand up and be coun - ted,

109

If I Were A Bell

Words & Music by Frank Loesser

That's the way I've just got to be-have____ Boy, if
From the won-der-ful way that you looked____ Boy, if

I were a lamp I'd light____ Or if I____ were a ban-ner I'd wave.
I were a duck I'd quack____ Or if I____ were a goose____ I'd be cooked.

Ask me how do I feel,____ Lit - tle me with my qui-et up-
Ask me how do I feel,____ Ask me now that we're fond-ly ca-

bring - ing _____ Well sir, all I can say____ is if I
ress - ing _____ Pal, if I were a sal - ad I know____

I'll Never Fall In Love Again

Words by Hal David
Music by Burt Bacharach

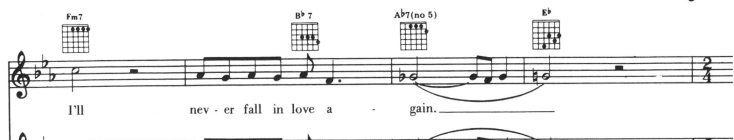

I'll nev-er fall in love a-gain.____

Don't tell me what it's all a-bout,____ 'Cause I've been there__ and I'm

glad I'm out;____ Out of those chains, those chains that bind__ you, That is why I'm

here to re-mind__ you.
here to re-mind you. What do you get when you fall in love,____ You

116

Is You Is, Or Is You Ain't (Ma' Baby)

Words & Music by Billy Austin & Louis Jordan

Is you is or is you ain't my ba - by?___ The

way you're act - ing late - ly makes me doubt.___

Is___ you is or is you ain't my ba - by?___

Seems my flame in your heart's done gone out.___ My

friends say I could do a lot bet - ter, — if this keeps up I'll soon need a nurse. — I

know I can't do a - ny bet - ter, — but be - lieve me I could do a lot worse. —

Is — you is or is you ain't my ba - by? — The

way you're act - ing late - ly makes me doubt. —

Is__ you is or is you ain't my ba - by?_____

Seems my flame in your heart's done gone out._____ When the

moon goes down in the dawn - ing__ and the sun comes up in the morn -

- ing,__ don't let the sun catch you cry - in'. When the

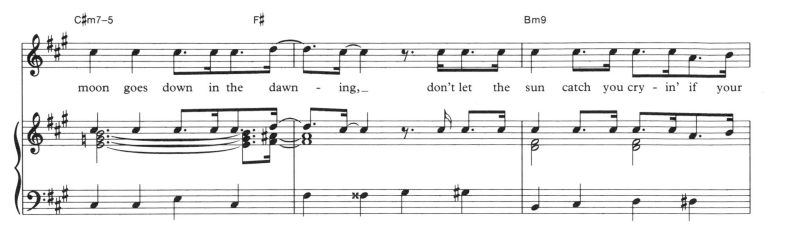

moon goes down in the dawn - ing,___ don't let the sun catch you cry - in' if your

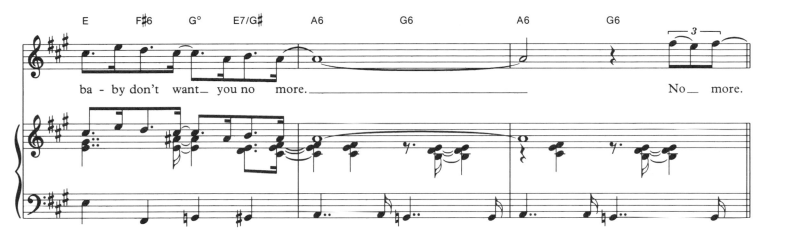

ba - by don't want___ you no more._____ No___ more.

No___ more._____

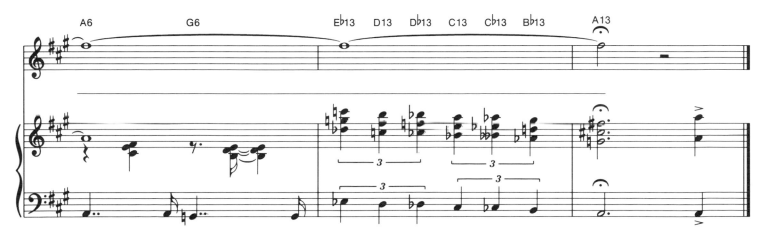

Love Changes Everything

Music by Andrew Lloyd Webber
Lyrics by Don Black & Charles Hart

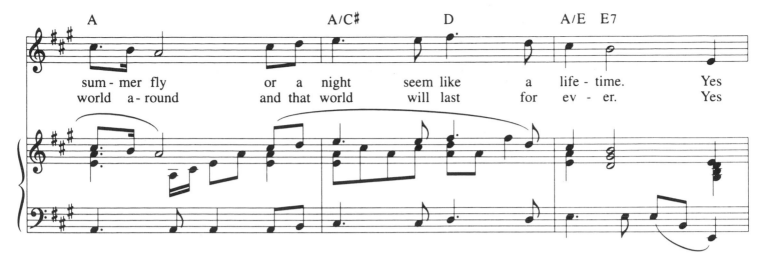

sum - mer fly　　　or a night　seem like　　a life - time.　Yes
world a - round　and that world　will last　for ev - er.　Yes

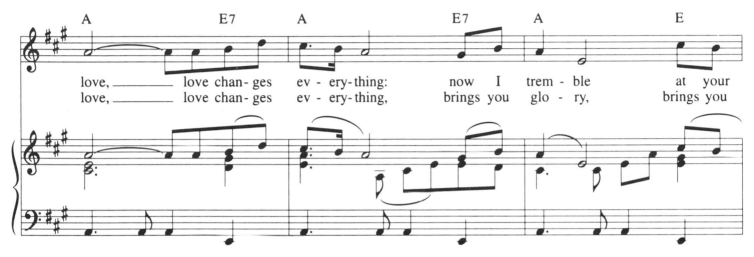

love, _____ love chan - ges ev - ery-thing:　now I trem - ble　at your
love, _____ love chan - ges ev - ery-thing,　brings you glo - ry,　brings you

name.　No-thing in the world will ev - er be　the
shame.　No-thing in the world will ev - er be　the

1. same.

2. same. _____

Off _____ in-to the world we go, plan-ning fu-tures, shap-ing years.

Love _____ bursts in and sud-den-ly, all our wis-dom dis-ap-pears.

Love _____ makes fools of ev-ery-one: all the rules we make are

124

Luck Be A Lady

Words & Music by Frank Loesser

Moderately

They call you La-dy Luck but there is room for doubt At

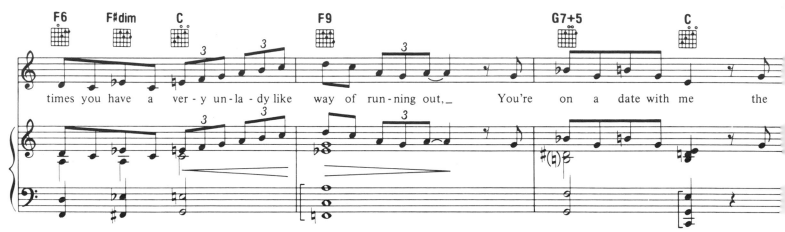

times you have a ver-y un-la-dy like way of run-ning out,_ You're on a date with me the

pick-ings have been lush And yet be-fore this eve-ning is ov-er you might give me the brush._ You

might for-get your man-ners, you might re-fuse to stay, And so the best that I can do is

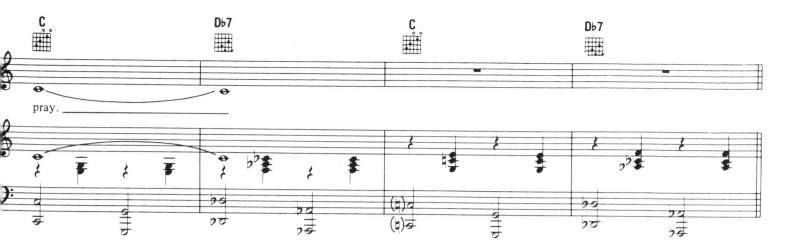

pray. _____

Luck Be A La - dy to - night _____

Luck Be A La - dy to - night _____

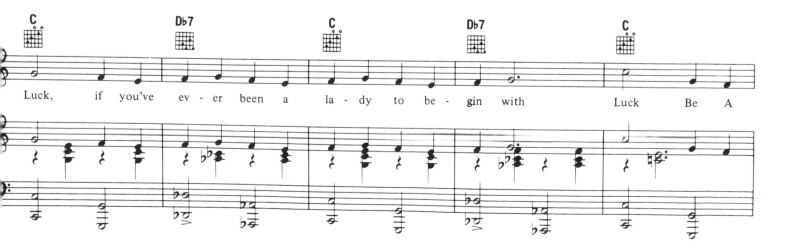

Luck, if you've ev - er been a la - dy to be - gin with Luck Be A

127

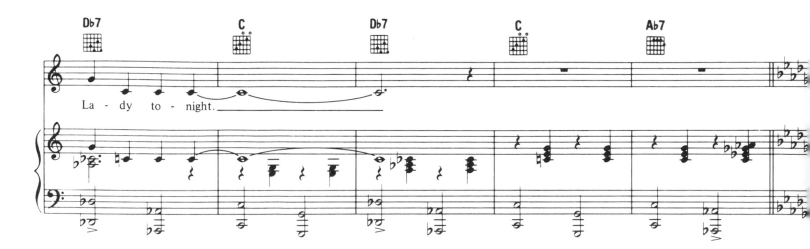

La - dy to - night. _____

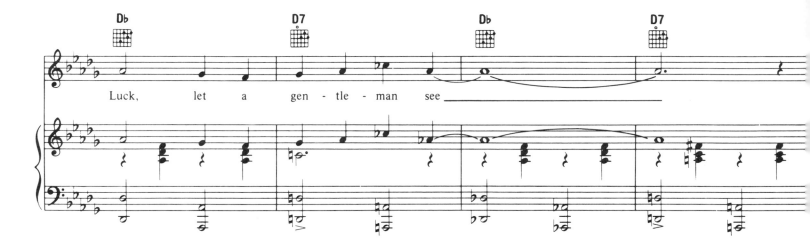

Luck, let a gen - tle - man see _____

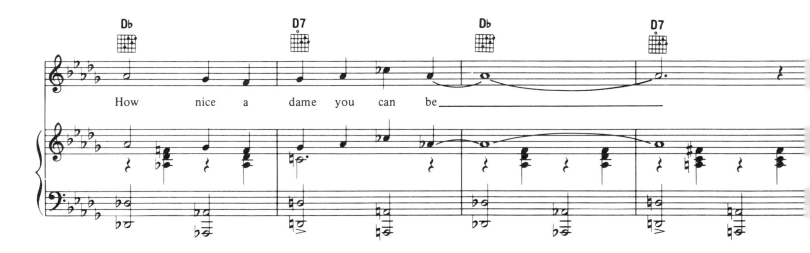

How nice a dame you can be _____

I know they say you've treat - ed oth - er guys you've been with Luck Be A

128

let's keep the par - ty po - lite _____

Nev - er get out of my sight _____ Stick with me

ba - by I'm the fel - low you came in with, Luck Be A La - dy,

Luck Be A La - dy, Luck Be A La - dy to - night. _____

130

Martin Guerre

Music by Claude-Michel Schönberg
Lyrics by Alain Boublil, Edward Hardy & Herbert Kretzmer

E-nough, no more, I don't give a damn. Why stay? What for? I know who I am. A man a-bove the lie that we

live. A man who'll love when he's read-y to give. But I'll come back one day af-ter ten years a-

way and they'll stop and they'll say look…

Poco piu mosso

(Spoken)…Look…

Look,_____ it's— Mar-tin

same, but by hea-ven they're sure to— see there's more to——Mar-tin Guerre than a

name. And that bas-tard Pi-erre,

holds my life in his hands. He's no un-cle of mine. He can have all my land. The

land he sold me for. May God con-demn his soul to hell and all of Ar-ti-gat as well.

Matchmaker

Words by Sheldon Harnick
Music by Jerry Bock

book and make me a per - fect match.
book and make her a per - fect match.

Match - mak - er, match - mak - er, { I'll bring the veil, you bring the
{ you know that I'm still ve - ry
Match - mak - er, match - mak - er, we'll bring the veil, you bring the

{ groom, slen - der and pale. Bring me a ring, for I'm
young, please take your time. Up to this min - ute, I
groom, slen - der and pale. Bring her a ring, for she's

{ long - ing to be the en - vy of all I see.
mis - un - der - stood that I could be all stuck for good.
long - ing to be the en - vy of all she'll see.

2° To Coda ⊕

Match - mak - er, match - mak - er, make me a match, find me a
Match - mak - er, match - mak - er, make her a match, find her a

find, catch me a catch. Night af - ter night in the
find, catch her a catch. Night af - ter night in the

dark I'm a - lone, so strike me a match of
dark she's a - lone, so find her a match of

my own.
her own. *(end of male vocal)*

D.%. al Coda

Maybe This Time

Music by John Kander
Lyrics by Fred Ebb

He will hold me fast. I'll be home at last.

Not a los-er___ an-y-more,___ like the last time___ and the time be-fore.___

Ev-'ry-bo-dy___ loves a win-ner___ so no-bo-dy___ loved me.

La-dy Peace-ful.___ La-dy Hap-py.___ That's what I long___ to be.

that's what I long_ to be.　　All the odds are_ in my fa-vour,_ some-thing's bound_ to be-gin.

It's_ got to hap-pen,_ hap-pen some-time,_ may-be this time,_ may-be this time_ I'll win._

My Darling, My Darling
Words & Music by Frank Loesser

One Night In Bangkok

Words & Music by Benny Andersson, Tim Rice & Bjorn Ulvaeus

All change — don't you know that when you play at this lev-el there's no or-di-na-ry ven-ue.
let you watch, I would in-vite you but the queens we use would not ex-cite you.

It's Ice - land — or the Phil-ip-pines — or Has - tings —
So you'd better go back to your bars, your tem - ples,

or — or this place!
- sage par-lours —

Choir

One night in Bang-kok and the world's your

oys - ter, the bars are tem - ples but the pearls ain't free.

*Piano top line also vocal top line.

You'll find a god in ev - ery gold - en _____ clois - ter and if you're
luck - y then the god's a she. _____ I can feel an an - gel slid - ing up to me.

The American   *Choir*

One town's ve - ry like an - oth - er when your head's down ov - er your pie - ces, broth - er. It's a

drag, it's a bore, it's real - ly such a pi - ty to be look - ing at the board, not look - ing at the ci - ty.

153

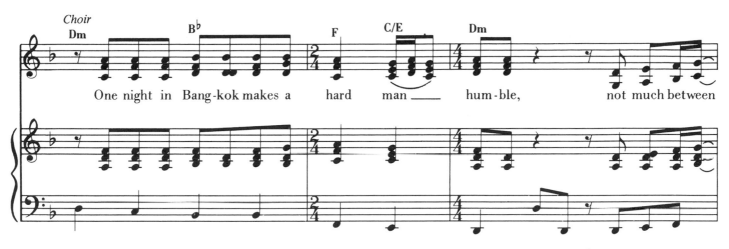

One night in Bang-kok makes a hard man _____ hum-ble, not much between

de - spair and ec - sta - sy. _____ One night in Bang-kok and the

tough guys _____ tum - ble, can't be too care - ful with your com-pa - ny.

_____ I can feel the dev - il walk-ing next to me. _____

hum-ble, not much be-tween de-spair and ec - sta - sy.

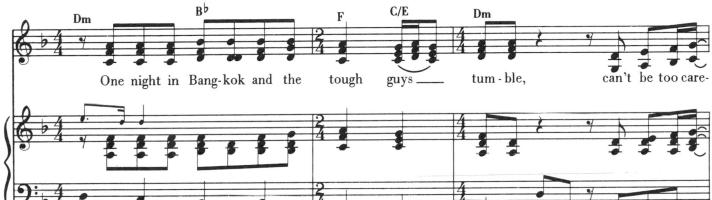

One night in Bang-kok and the tough guys ___ tum - ble, can't be too care-

-ful with your com-pa - ny. ___ I can feel the dev-

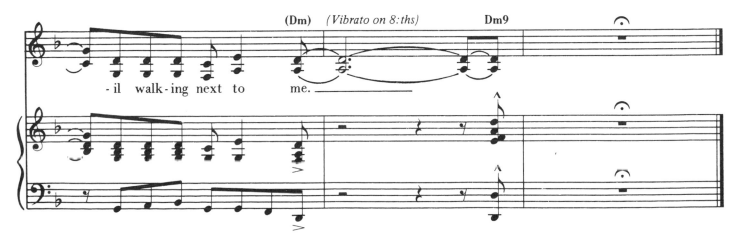

-il walk-ing next to me. ___

(Vibrato on 8:ths)

Ol' Man River

Music by Jerome Kern
Words by Oscar Hammerstein II

Slowly

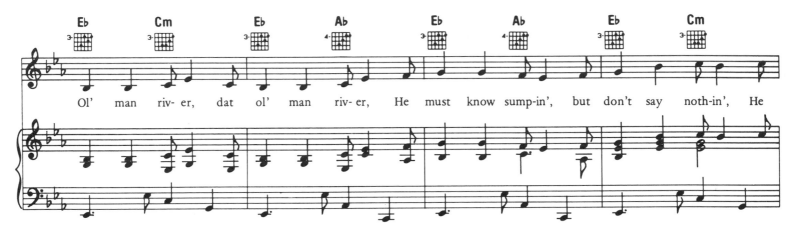

Ol' man riv-er, dat ol' man riv-er, He must know sump-in', but don't say noth-in', He

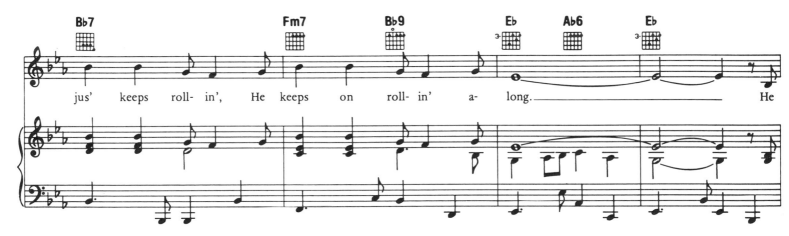

jus' keeps roll-in', He keeps on roll-in' a-long._____ He

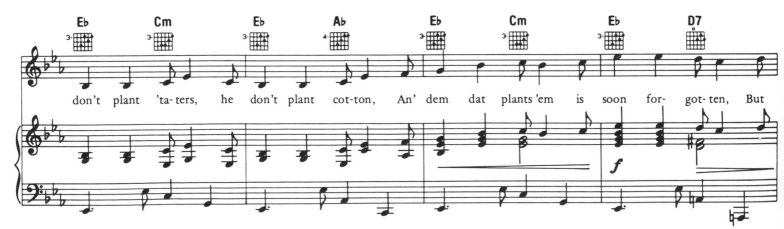

don't plant 'ta-ters, he don't plant cot-ton, An' dem dat plants 'em is soon for-got-ten, But

Promises Promises

Music by Burt Bacharach
Lyrics by Hal David

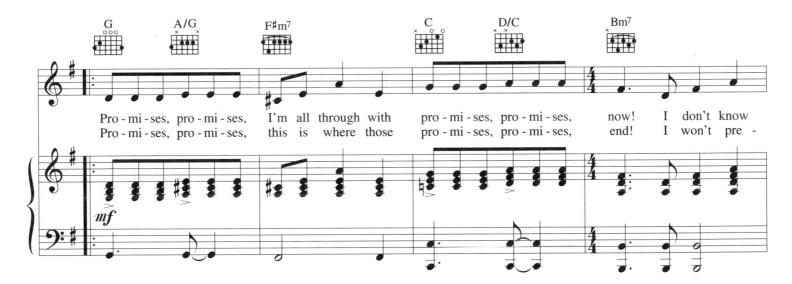

Pro - mi - ses, pro - mi - ses, I'm all through with pro - mi - ses, pro - mi - ses, now! I don't know
Pro - mi - ses, pro - mi - ses, this is where those pro - mi - ses, pro - mi - ses, end! I won't pre -

how I got the nerve to walk out.
tend that what was wrong can be right.

160

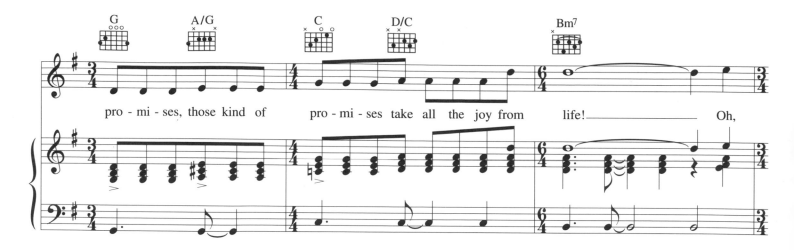

pro - mi - ses, those kind of pro - mi - ses take all the joy from life!_____ Oh,

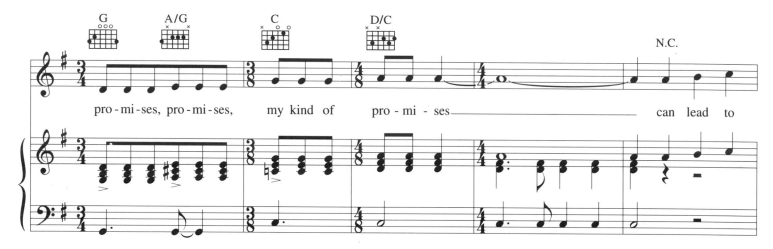

pro - mi - ses, pro - mi - ses, my kind of pro - mi - ses_____ can lead to

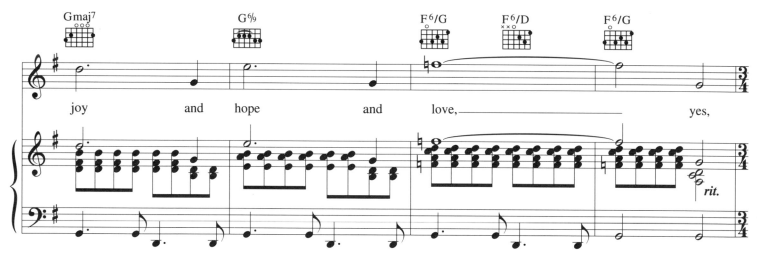

joy and hope and love,_____ yes,

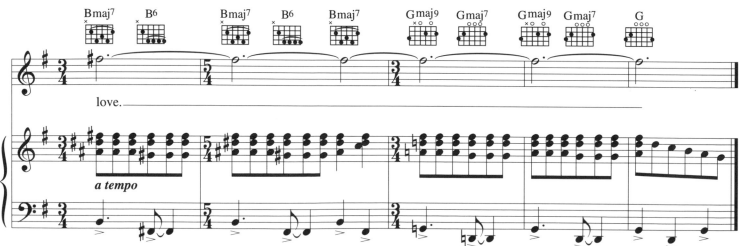

love._____

Some Enchanted Evening

Words by Oscar Hammerstein II
Music by Richard Rodgers

165

Seventy Six Trombones

Words & Music by Meredith Willson

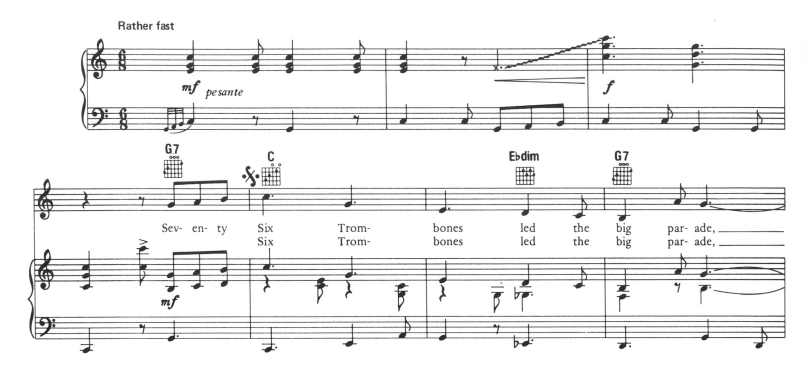

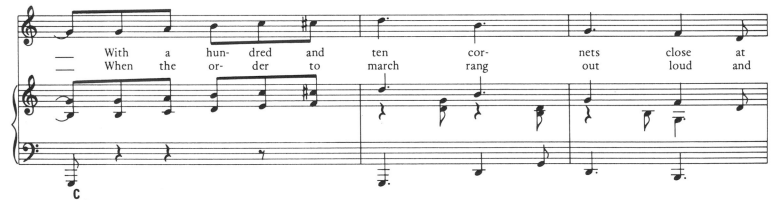

having his big fat say. There were trum-pet-ers who'd

im-pro-vise a full oc-tave high-er than the score.

D.S. al Coda

Sev-en-ty

D.S. al Coda

CODA

one and on-ly bass, And I

oom-pahed, oom-pahed, oom-pah-pahed

oom-pahed up and down the square.

Standing On The Corner

Words & Music by Frank Loesser

Sunrise Sunset

Words by Sheldon Harnick
Music by Jerry Bock

Moderately slow waltz tempo (*soulful and wistful*)

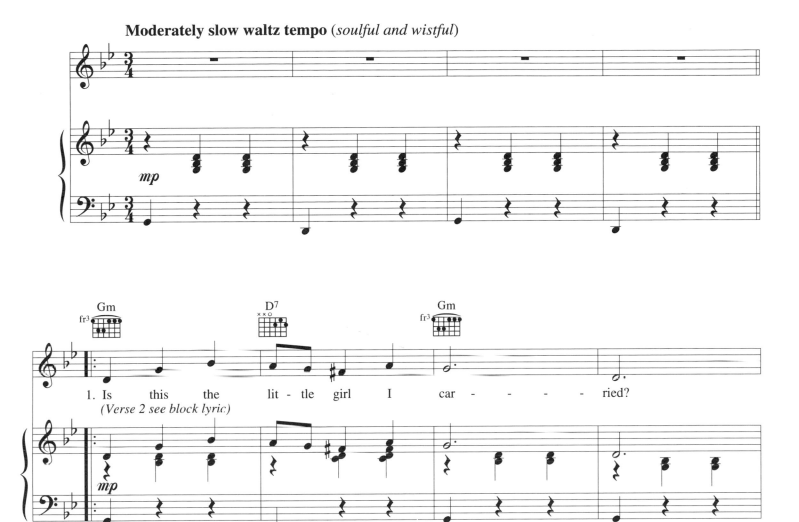

1. Is this the lit – tle girl I car - - - ried?
(Verse 2 see block lyric)

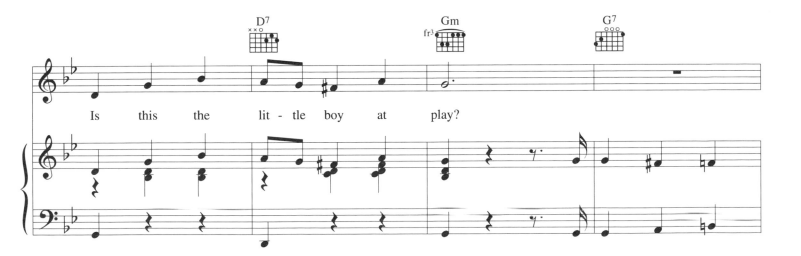

Is this the lit – tle boy at play?

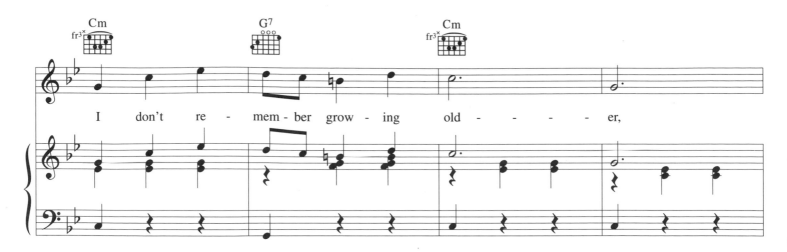

I don't re - mem - ber grow - ing old - - - - er,

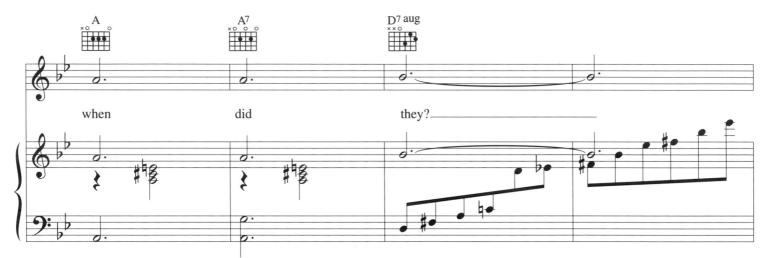

when did they?_____

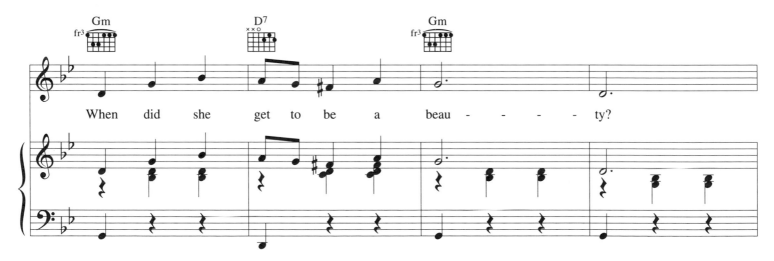

When did she get to be a beau - - - ty?

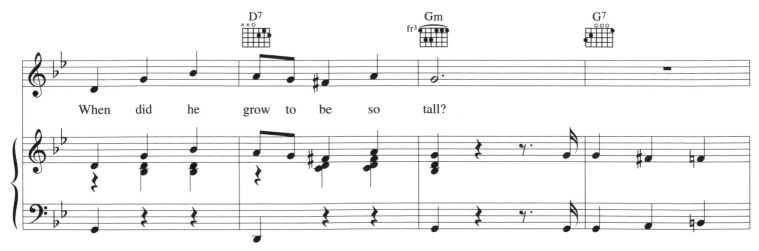

When did he grow to be so tall?

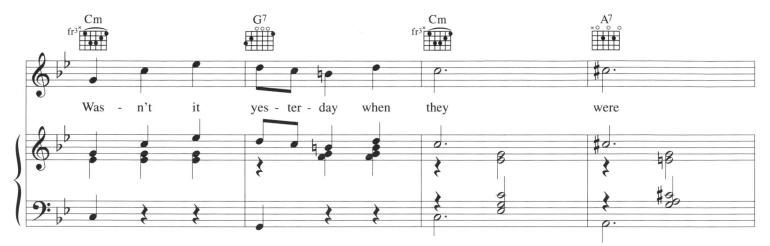

Was - n't it yes - ter - day when they were

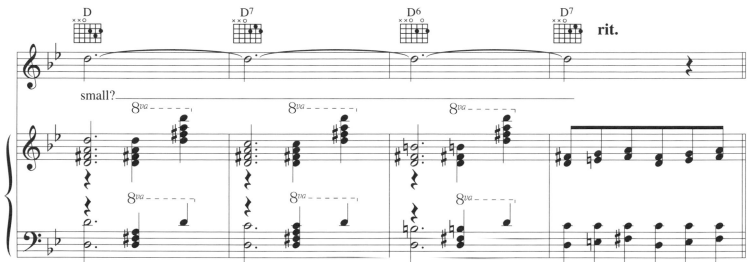

small?

rit.

a tempo

Sun - rise, sun - set, sun - rise, sun - set,

mp - mf

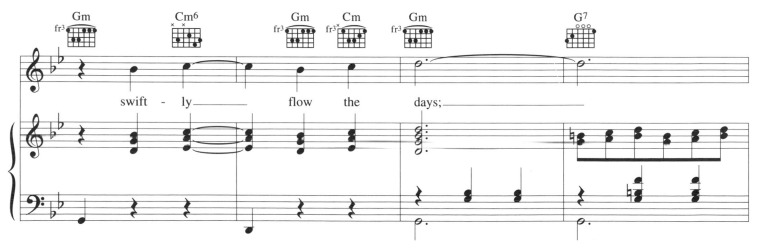

swift - ly flow the days;

175

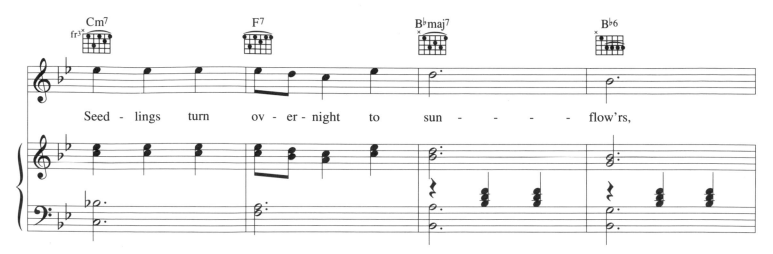

Seed - lings turn ov - er - night to sun - - - - flow'rs,

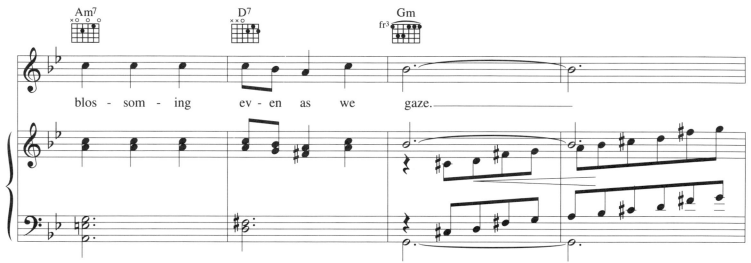

blos - som - ing ev - en as we gaze.

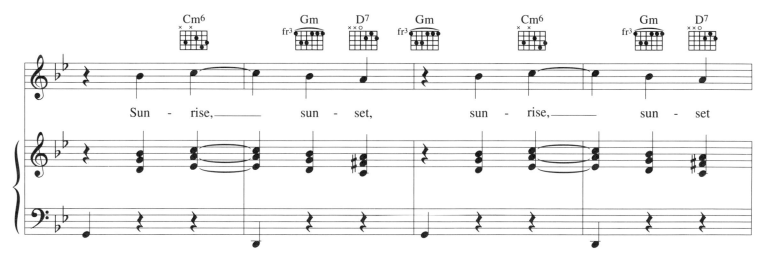

Sun - rise, _____ sun - set, _____ sun - rise, _____ sun - set

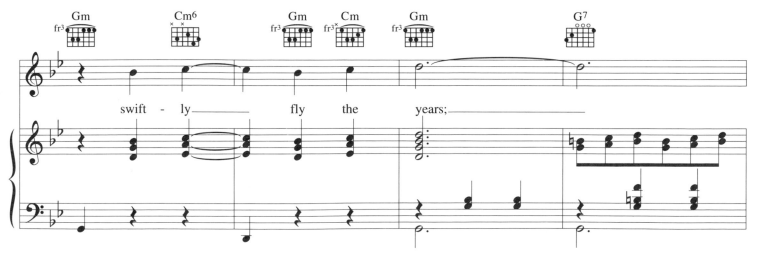

swift - ly _____ fly the years; _____

Verse 2:
Now is the little boy a bridegroom
Now is the little girl a bride
Under the canopy I see them side by side.
Place the gold ring around her finger
Share the sweet wine and break the glass
Soon the full circle will have come to pass.

Take That Look Off Your Face

Music by Andrew Lloyd Webber
Lyrics by Don Black

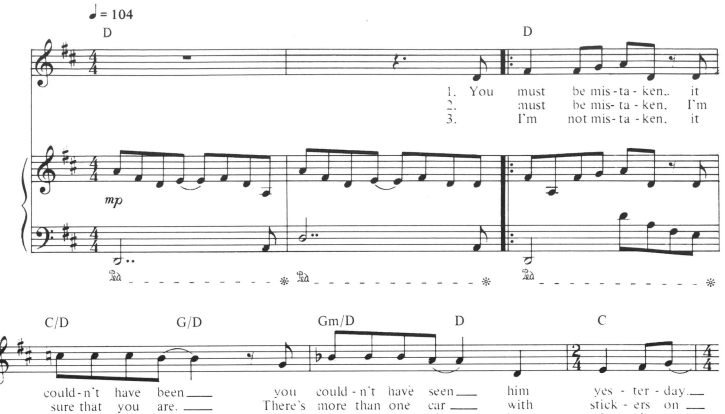

1. You must be mis-ta-ken, it
2. must be mis-ta-ken, I'm
3. I'm not mis-ta-ken, it

could-n't have been____ you could-n't have seen____ him yes-ter-day.____
sure that you are.____ There's more than one car____ with stick-ers on____
start-ed last year.____ I'm not ve-ry clear____ how it be-gan____

____ He's do-ing some deal____ up in Bal-ti-more now,____ I
and lots of young guys____ wear cor-du-roy pants____ and I'd
____ I not-iced a change____ but I just closed my eyes____ as

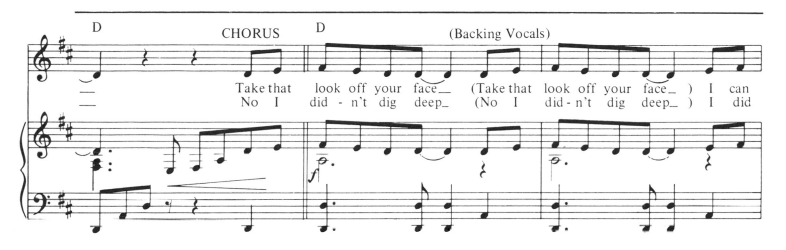

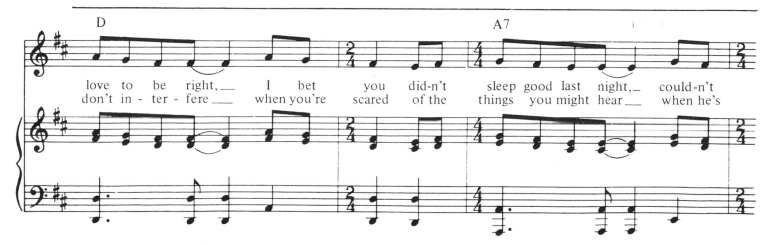

see through your smile,___ you would love to be right,___ I bet

you did-n't sleep good last night___ could-n't wait to bring

all of that bad___ news to my door, well I've got news for you___

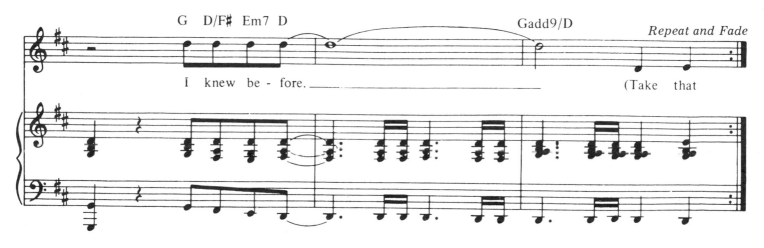

I knew be-fore._____ (Take that

The Rhythm Of Life

Words by Dorothy Fields
Music by Cy Coleman

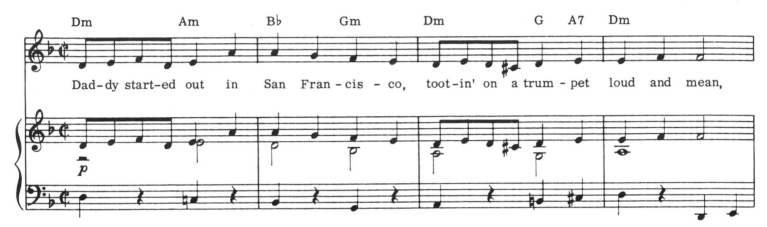

Dad-dy start-ed out in San Fran-cis-co, toot-in' on a trum-pet loud and mean,

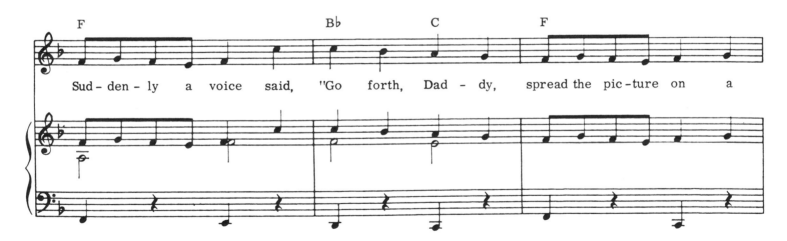

Sud-den-ly a voice said, "Go forth, Dad-dy, spread the pic-ture on a

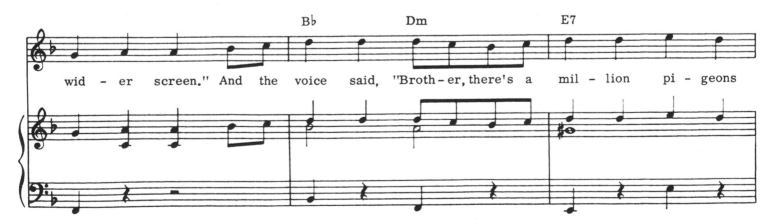

wid-er screen." And the voice said, "Broth-er, there's a mil-lion pi-geons

ready to be hooked on new religions. Hit the road, Daddy, leave your

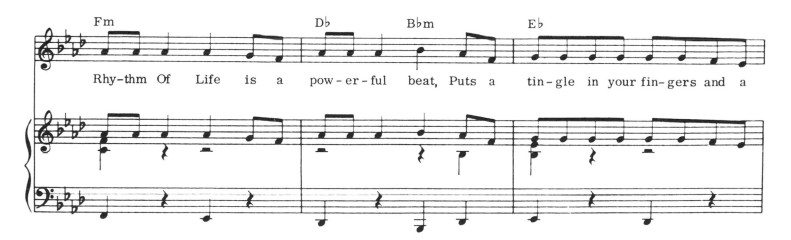

common-law wife. Spread the religion of The Rhythm Of Life." And The

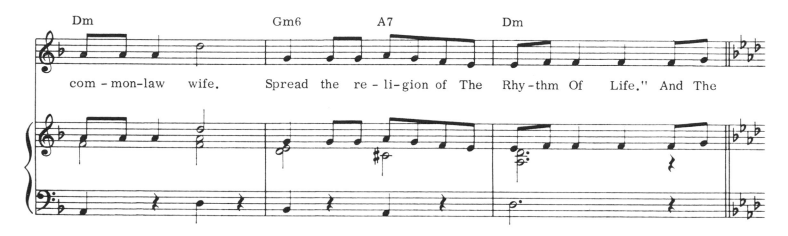

Rhythm Of Life is a powerful beat, Puts a tingle in your fingers and a

tingle in your feet, Rhythm in your bedroom, rhythm in the street, Yes, The

Rhy-thm Of Life is a pow-er-ful beat. To feel the

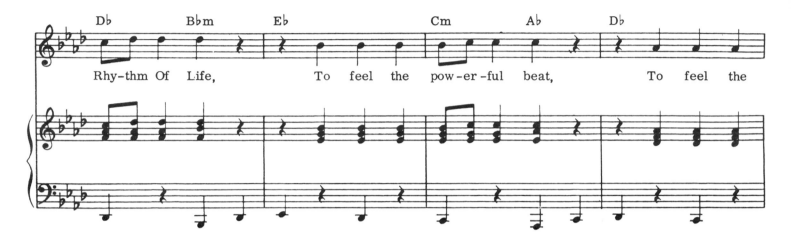

Rhy-thm Of Life, To feel the pow-er-ful beat, To feel the

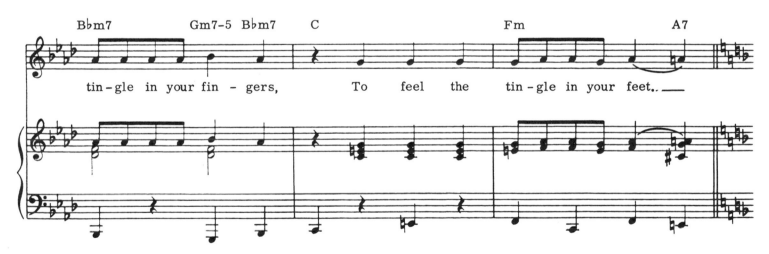

tin-gle in your fin - gers, To feel the tin-gle in your feet. ___

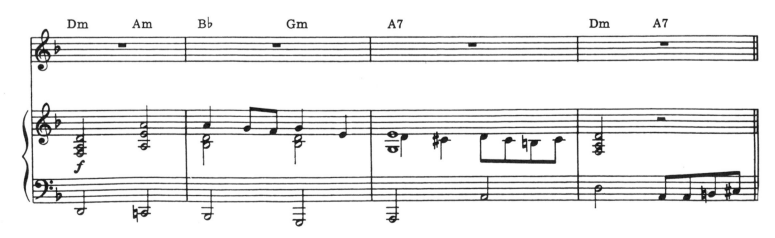

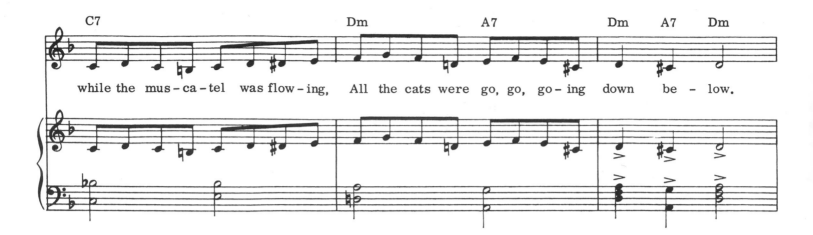

while the mus-ca-tel was flow-ing, All the cats were go, go, go-ing down be - low.

Dad-dy was a new sen - sa-tion, Got him-self a con-gre-ga-tion,

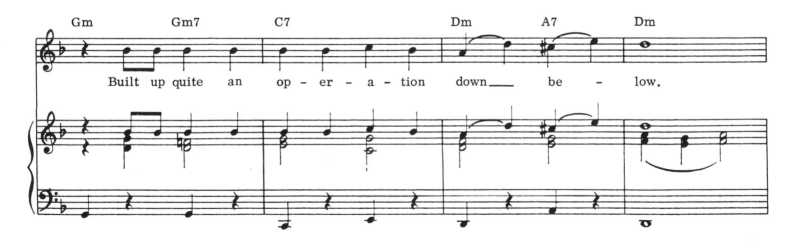

Built up quite an op - er - a - tion down___ be - low.

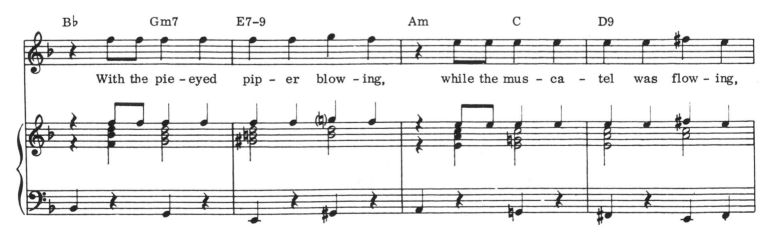

With the pie - eyed pip - er blow - ing, while the mus - ca - tel was flow - ing,

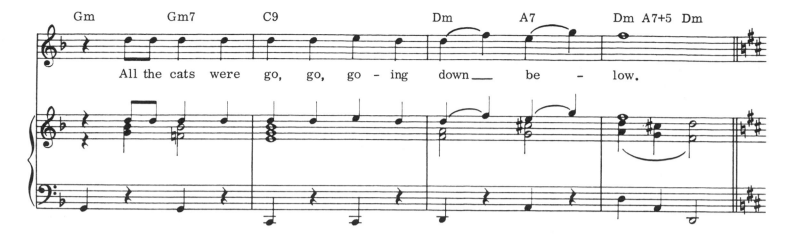

All the cats were go, go, go-ing down___ be - low.

Flip your wings and fly to Dad-dy, Flip your wings and fly to Dad-dy,

Flip your wings and fly to Dad-dy, Fly,___ fly,___ fly to Dad-dy.

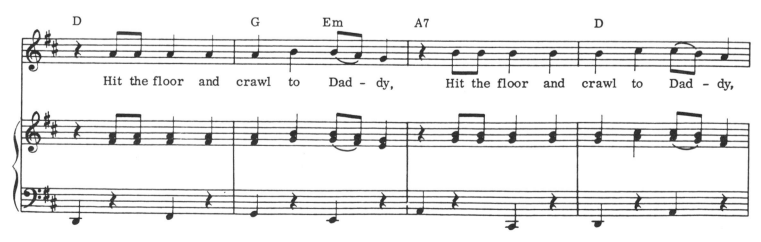

Hit the floor and crawl to Dad-dy, Hit the floor and crawl to Dad-dy,

Hit the floor and crawl to Dad - dy, Crawl,_ crawl,_ crawl to Dad - dy.

To feel The Rhy - thm Of Life, To feel the pow - er - ful beat,

To feel the rhy - thm in your fin - gers, To feel the tin - gle in your feet._

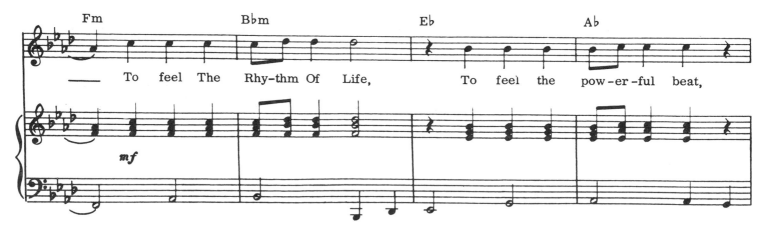

_ To feel The Rhy - thm Of Life, To feel the pow - er - ful beat,

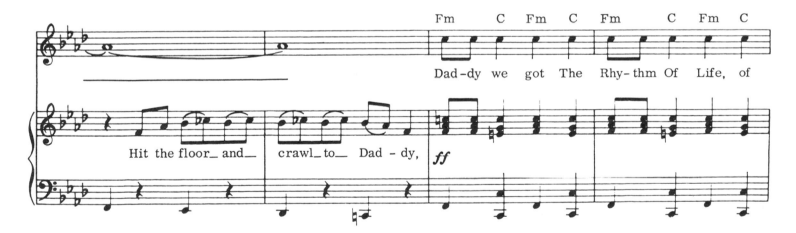

189

'Til Tomorrow

Music by Jerry Bock
Lyrics by Sheldon Harnick

Gently

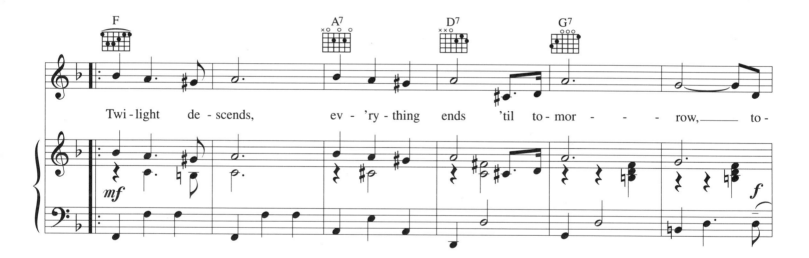

Twi-light de-scends, ev-'ry-thing ends 'til to-mor - - - row,——— to-

mor - - - row.   Since we must part,   here is my heart, 'til to-

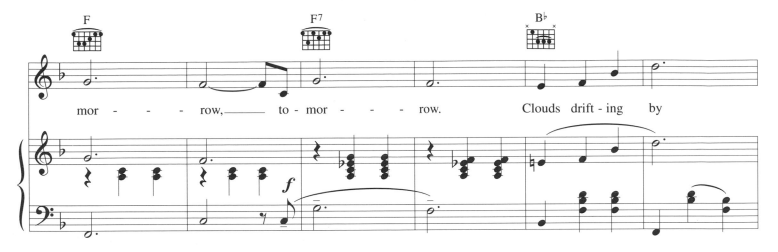

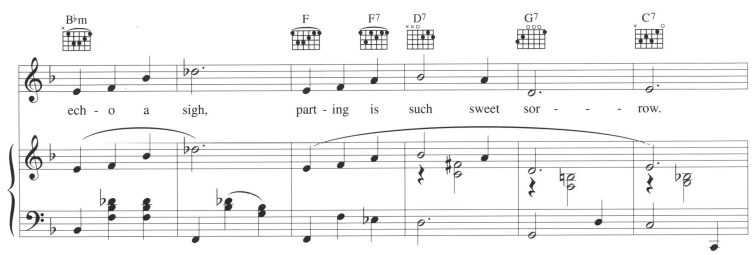

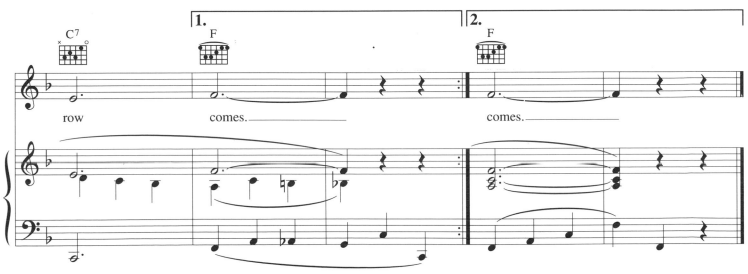

Tomorrow

Music by Charles Strouse
Words by Martin Charnin

What Kind Of Fool Am I

Words & Music by Leslie Bricusse & Anthony Newley

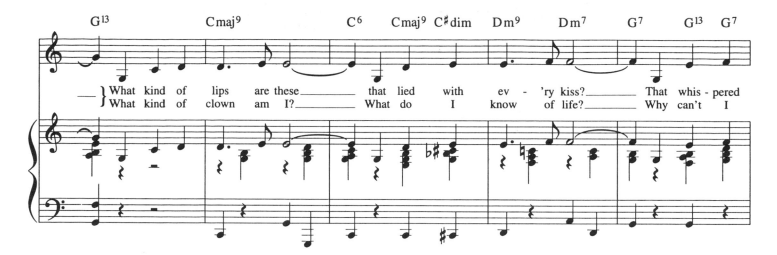

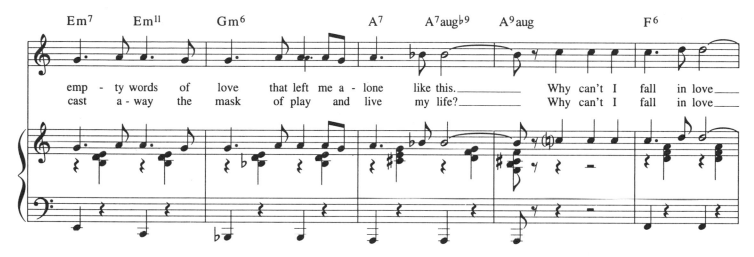

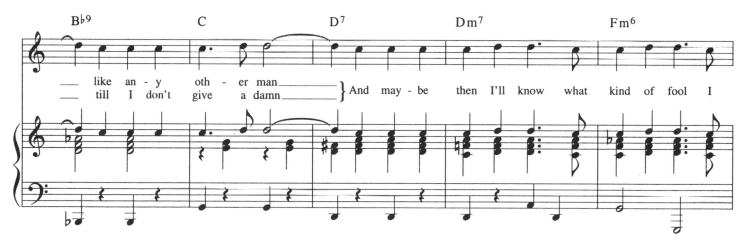

When Will Someone Hear?

Music by Claude-Michel Schönberg
Lyrics by Alain Boublil & Stephen Clark

When will some-one hear?_

All I know is fear._ And now I see the lone-li-ness of lo-sing all you trust._

Day has turned to night, stone has turned to dust. And now I need to find the words._

When will some-one hear? Love that once was close,— faith that once was clear.—

Now all I've known and all I've loved is all I have to grieve.—

All that I've be-gun, all that I be-lieve is just a-no-ther bro-ken dream.—

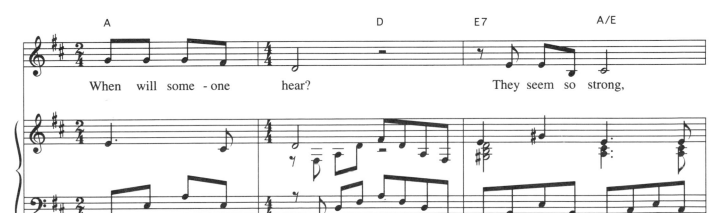

When will some-one hear? They seem so strong,

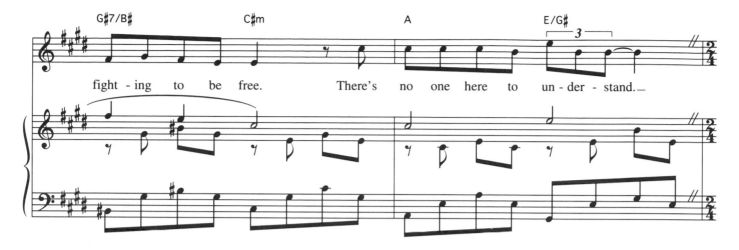

fight - ing to be free. There's no one here to un - der - stand.—

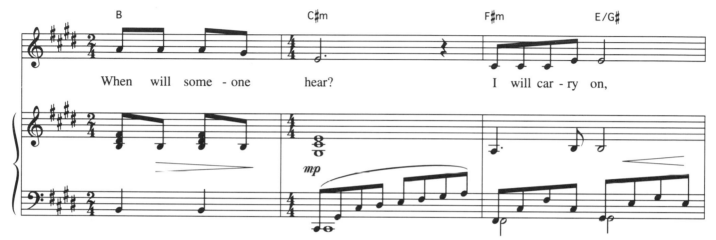

When will some - one hear? I will car - ry on,

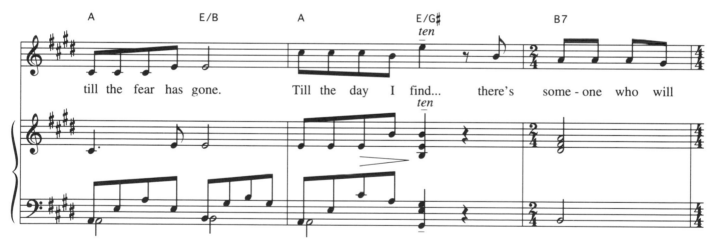

till the fear has gone. Till the day I find... there's some - one who will

hear.

With One Look

Music by Andrew Lloyd Webber
Lyrics by Don Black & Christopher Hampton
with contributions by Amy Powers

Si - lent mu-sic starts to play. One tear in my eye makes the whole world cry.

With one look they'll for - give the past, they'll re - joice I've re-turned at last

to my peo-ple in the dark, still out there in the dark.

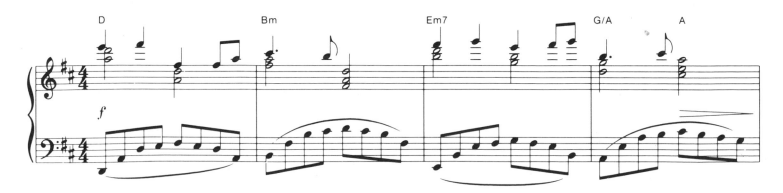

The Music Of The Night

Music by Andrew Lloyd Webber
Lyrics by Charles Hart. Additional lyrics by Richard Stilgoe

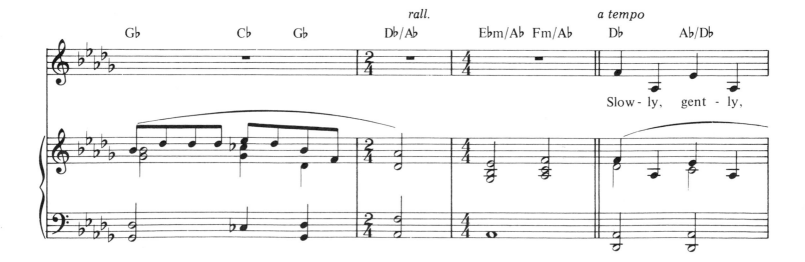

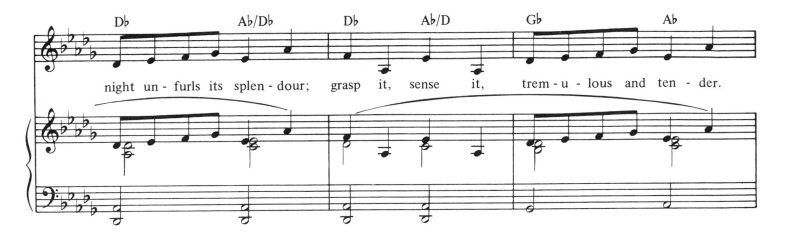

night un-furls its splen-dour; grasp it, sense it, trem-u-lous and ten-der.

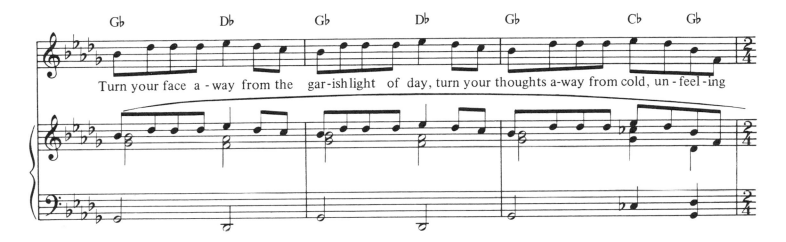

Turn your face a-way from the gar-ish light of day, turn your thoughts a-way from cold, un-feel-ing

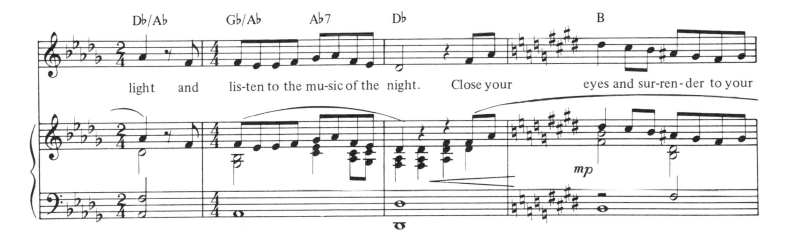

light and lis-ten to the mu-sic of the night. Close your eyes and sur-ren-der to your

dark-est dreams! Purge your thoughts of the life you knew be - fore! Close your

eyes let your spi-rit start to soar and you'll live as you've nev-er lived be - fore.

Soft - ly, deft - ly, mu - sic shall ca - ress you. Hear it, feel it,

se -cret-ly po-ssess you. O-pen up your mind let your fan-ta-sies un-wind in this

dark-ness which you know you can - not fight, the dark-ness of the mu -sic of the

9/01(41375)